Medicina Natural

LA HOMEOPATIA

Dra. Carmen Reyes Pérez García
Dra. María José Lucio López

LIBSA

© 1993. LIBSA

Editorial LIBSA
Narciso Serra, 25
28007 Madrid
Telf.: 433 54 07
Fax: 433 02 04

Imprime: Mateu Cromo, S.A.
ISBN: 84-7630-240-1
Depósito Legal: M. 39735 - 1994

«En el arte de curar, dejar de aprender es un crimen.»

C. S. F. Hahnemann

l problema que la Medicina se plantea actualmente, tras el cientifismo exacerbado del siglo XX, es la ausencia de una visión integral y humanista de la persona, en todos sus ámbitos y circunstancias. La «superespecialización» ha conducido a la fragmentación del enfermo, y cada especialista tiene un conocimiento profundo sólo de una parcela, careciendo de una visión global del individuo.

La Homeopatía no cura al enfermo por «por partes» o por corrección local, ya que contempla al sujeto de forma integral, teniendo en cuenta todos y cada uno de los síntomas, para remitirlos a un contexto individual y diferente en cada persona.

La Homeopatía —del griego «homios»: semejante y «pathos»: padecimiento o enfermedad— es una forma de tratamiento médico, que se realiza mediante sustancias capaces de producir en el hombre sano trastornos semejantes a los de la enfermedad que se va a combatir, siendo éste su fundamento, es decir, la Ley de Similitud, expresada por el término latino «Similia similibus curantur» —los semejantes se curan con los semejantes—. La administración de estas sustancias se hace a dosis muy pequeñas (infinitesimales), carentes de toxicidad.

La Alopatía, o medicina tradicional, basa sus tratamientos en la curación por los contrarios, como se define en el lema «Contraria contrariis curantur» —los contrarios se curan con los contrarios— y utiliza medicamentos a dosis ponderables.

Es bien conocido que el café produce, en el individuo sano, un estado de excitación física y mental e insomnio. Pues bien, en Homeopatía, para tratar el insomnio, se puede usar esta misma

El café, generador de insomnio, es una sustancia que en dosis muy pequeñas y bajo preparaciones adecuadas, se utiliza en homeopatía para tratarlo.

sustancia (Coffea) que, en dosis muy pequeñas y preparada de una manera particular, harían desaparecer las molestias sin provocar ningún efecto indeseable.

En Alopatía, para combatir el insomnio, se utilizan sustancias que producen el efecto contrario, como ansiolíticos, barbitúricos...

Vemos pues, que se trata de dos visiones diferentes, cuyas bases fisiológicas son opuestas y que, ya desde la antigüedad, han tenido su aceptación, bien por separado o a la vez, en el terreno de la patología.

El padre de la Homeopatía es C. F. S. HAHNEMANN, quien en el siglo XVIII, afirma la actividad de las dosis infinitesimales, muchos años antes de que las investigaciones confirmaran que la acción de cantidades infinitamente pequeñas de sustancias (vitaminas, prostaglandinas, fermentos...) es una realidad.

El camino por él marcado, permanecerá mucho tiempo en la heterodoxia, entrando hoy, por pleno derecho, en la comunidad médica científica. La Homeopatía cuenta actualmente con laboratorios, investigadores y experimentación rigurosa, habiendo alcanzado un importante nivel y difusión en países como Francia (donde está incluida dentro de la Sanidad Pública), Inglaterra, Alemania, Suiza, Argentina, Méjico ...

La Homeopatía es una medicina REACTIVA. Esto quiere decir que estimula la capacidad de reacción del organismo frente a la enfermedad. Debido a las pequeñas dosis utilizadas, carece de efectos indeseables, por lo que constituye una forma de tratamiento ideal en todas las edades y personas —niños, embarazadas...

La terapia homeopática es totalmente individualizada, ya que cada sujeto confiere a la enfermedad sus características personales y así, dos individuos con el mismo diagnóstico no sufren su padecimiento de la misma manera, y su tratamiento, por tanto, será diferente.

Los procesos agudos pueden ser combatidos con resultados sorprendentemente rápidos en muchas ocasiones. Pero es en el campo de las patologías crónicas y recurrentes donde la Homeopatía aporta mayores ventajas, ya que, por actuar sobre el individuo en conjunto, modificando su predisposición a padecer determinadas enfermedades, no sólo suprimirá los síntomas durante un tiempo, sino que curará el proceso.

Antecedentes históricos de la Homeopatía

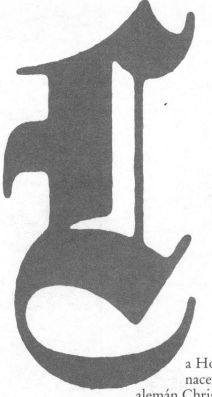

a Homeopatía, como tal disciplina, nace en el siglo XVIII con el médico alemán Christian-Friedrich Samuel Hahnemann, que enunció sus principios fundamentales. Sin embargo, sus ideas tenían precedentes a lo largo de la historia.

La Escuela Hipocrática, cuyo iniciador fue Hipócrates, en el siglo V a.C., máxima figura de la Medicina en la Antigüedad, preconiza la observación del enfermo como base del saber médico, eliminando las supersticiones en torno a la enfermedad, existentes en su época. El método utilizado por esta escuela se basa en la experiencia, como se observa al leer los tratados hipocráticos, en los que se encuentra una detallada anotación del cuadro clínico del enfermo, que produce la sensación de inmediato contacto con él. Estas recopilaciones de datos constituyen las primeras historias clínicas dignas de tal nombre en la Medicina.

Los hipocráticos utilizaron, tanto tratamientos «por el contrario» —tendencia que la Medicina ha mantenido hasta la actualidad—, como «por el similar» —«por el

*Hipócrates, máxima figura
de la Medicina en la Antigüedad*

*Teofrasto Paracelso (1493-1541).
Médico y alquimista.*

similar la enfermedad se desarrolla y por el empleo del similar la enfermedad es curada»—, sin perder de vista en ningún momento la individualización del tratamiento. No sólo tienen en cuenta la índole de la enfermedad, sino también la constitución del enfermo, sexo, estación del año, ...

Paracelso, en el siglo XV, dedicado al estudio conjunto de medicina y alquimia, utilizó una serie de principios que han sido confirmados con el tiempo. Dió valor al remedio único y a las dosis ínfimas del mismo: marcó el comienzo de una terminología médica que individualizaba al paciente, llamando a las enfermedades por el nombre del remedio empleado en cada caso.

Esta terminología es utilizada habitualmente por la Homeopatía.

Pero el verdadero impulsor de la Homeopatía fue Hahnemann (1755-1843), médico de amplia cultura, apasionado por la química y la botánica y autor de más de cien libros.

En los tiempos de Hahnemann se pensaba que las enfermedades estaban producidas por impurezas de los humores (elementos constitutivos del organismo, según la creencia de la época), que era preciso eliminar de la forma que fuese, para llegar a la curación. Basándose en esta idea empleaban diuréticos, sudoríficos, vomitivos, purgantes, etc., que aumentaban la eliminación por vías naturales, o bien otros métodos que intentaban crear nuevas vías de eliminación: sangrías, cauterizaciones —con el fin de ocasionar quemaduras profundas, que se rellenaban luego con distintos materiales para provocar supuración—, vejigatorios —agentes productores de vesículas que después dejaban en «carne viva», sobre la que aplicaban otras sustancias que evitaban la cicatrización ...

Hahnemann, decepcionado por estas prácticas médicas que, más que curar, debilitaban o acababan con la vida de los enfermos, abandona el ejercicio de la medicina, trabajando durante muchos años como traductor, ya que dominaba varios idiomas (francés, inglés, italiano, entre otros).

A pesar de todo, animado por su deseo de saber, continuará buscando el medio para lograr la auténtica curación de las enfermedades. Traduciendo la Materia Médica de Cullen, descubre afirmaciones, sobre la acción de la quinina, que le parecen falsas y contradictorias, por lo que decide experimentar en sí mismo los efectos de esta droga. Así, observa que la administración de quinina durante varios días, le provoca todos los síntomas de la fiebre intermitente —paludismo—, efecto paradójico, ya que la quinina tiene la propiedad de suprimir la fiebre. Mediante este resultado, Hahnemann establece que «la quinina, que destruye la fiebre, provoca en un sujeto sano, la apariencia de la fiebre». Es su primera aproximación a la LEY DE SEMEJANZAS.

Durante años experimenta sistemáticamente, sobre sí mismo y sobre sus enfermos, los remedios y medicamentos del arsenal terapéutico de su tiempo. Tratando a un paciente con eléboro, comprende que la administración de dosis elevadas del remedio capaz de producir los mismos síntomas de la enfermedad a tratar, puede agravar el cuadro inicial. Es esta observación la que le da la pauta para ir disminuyendo progresivamente las dosis de los remedios empleados, llegando así al segundo principio de la Homeopatía: las DOSIS INFINITESIMALES.

Christian-Friedrich Samuel Hahnemann, fundador de la Homeopatía.

Da forma definitiva a las dos leyes de la Homeopatía en su libro «*Organon del arte de curar*», publicado en 1810, donde se puede leer: «Cualquier enfermedad sólo podrá ser eliminada de manera certera, rápida y duradera, mediante el remedio que, entre todos los posibles, sea el más capaz de producir en el estado de salud del hombre, la totalidad de los síntomas de tal enfermedad con la mayor semejanza posible...» y «las sustancias medicinales deben ser llevadas a un grado infinitesimal de dilución, dinamizándolas mediante su trituración y agitándolas adecuadamente...».

Hahnemann emplea, en la preparación de los remedios homeopáticos, sustancias vegetales, animales y minerales y las administra a un grupo, lo más amplio posible, de sujetos sanos. De esta forma, obtiene una serie de reacciones físicas y psíquicas de cada sujeto, que recoge bajo el nombre de **patogenesias**.

La quina le permitió descubrir a Hahnemann la «LEY DE LAS SEME JANZAS», primer principio de la Homeopatía. La «China» que es el remedio homeopático obtenido de la corteza del árbol de la quina, se utiliza mucho en homeopatía: en el tratamiento de pérdida de humores, estados graves de debilidad y para los convalecientes de enfermedades agotadoras, dolores periódicos de cabeza, neuralgias, bronquitis y tos ferina, taquicardia paroxismal, dolores de estómago, malas digestiones, dolencias biliares, fiebre, gota.

El tratamiento con eléboro o verdegambre le permitió a Hahnemann llegar al segundo principio de la Homeopatía: las DOSIS INFINITESIMALES. El remedio homeopático «Veratrum album» se usa frecuentemente para combatir las depresiones y otros trastornos psíquicos, la jaqueca y la bronquitis de las personas ancianas, las enfermedades circulatorias a consecuencia de infecciones, para la hipotensión acompañada de colapso y contra el infarto de miocardio, las diarreas, las intoxicaciones con alimentos, el lumbago, los calambres en las pantorrillas y las neuralgias.

Con estas minuciosas observaciones, introdujo un sistema científico, enteramente nuevo, para el estudio de las drogas. Es el primero en la historia de la Medicina que utiliza el **método experimental**.

Según sus conceptos, la enfermedad comienza con una alteración de la «fuerza vital», lo que da lugar a trastornos funcionales que, con el tiempo, pueden evolucionar hacia lesiones de los tejidos. Por tanto, la eliminación de la lesión orgánica, sin haber corregido previamente el desequilibrio de la fuerza vital que la originó, no conseguirá la curación real de la enfermedad sino solamente su desviación hacia otro órgano. La eliminación de un eczema (afección inflamatoria de la piel) mediante una pomada, sin preocuparse de más, no constituye una curación, debido a que la piel está enferma porque el organismo lo está.

Hahnemann, gracias a su enorme intuición y capacidad de trabajo, legó al mundo de la Medicina un sistema terapéutico mediante el cual podemos tratar, de manera suave y eficaz, la mayor parte de las enfermedades.

Principios básicos de la Homeopatía

l tratamiento homeopático se basa en la utilización de sustancias que, administradas a **dosis muy pequeñas**, son capaces de curar una determinada enfermedad, mientras que si fueran dadas en mayor cantidad a un individuo sano, le producirían unos **síntomas similares** a aquellos que se pretende combatir.

Imaginemos un paciente con una diarrea profusa, acuosa, sanguinolenta, con violento dolor abdominal y acompañada de gran postración, pulso débil y sudoración fría generalizada. Si este enfermo consultara a un médico homeópata, éste le administraría Arsénico, potente veneno capaz de causar, entre otras manifestaciones, precisamente, una diarrea con estas mismas características. Pero eso sí, la prescripción se haría en **dosis muy pequeñas**, bajo ningún punto de vista tóxicas.

En Farmacología, a menudo se observa el hecho de que las pequeñas y grandes dosis de una misma sustancia activa ejercen efectos opuestos sobre el organismo. Así ocurre en los siguientes casos:

La digital provoca, a dosis tóxicas, un ritmo cardíaco irregular y rápido; sin embargo, a dosis menores sirve como

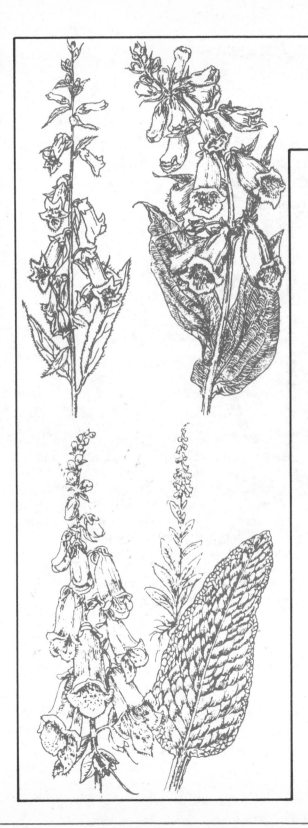

Digital: he aquí tres de las múltiples subespecies en las que se ha diversificado la antigua dedalera.

tratamiento para reforzar, retardar y regular los latidos cardíacos. Por otra parte, los síntomas provocados por una sobredosis de digitálicos son muy parecidos a los trastornos cardíacos en los que estaría indicado su uso.

El alcohol, en pequeñas cantidades, es estimulante, pero en mayor cuantía produce depresión y somnolencia, pudiendo llegar al coma.

El mercurio y sus sales provocan, a dosis tóxicas, oliguria o anuria (es decir, disminución o ausencia completa de la diuresis o excreción urinaria). No obstante, se han utilizado hasta hace pocos años, diuréticos mercuriales para tratar la oliguria.

En alergología se emplean como desensibilizantes, en pequeñas dosis, las mismas sustancias que en cantidades mayores son capaces de provocar reacciones alérgicas.

La medicina tradicional, por tanto, recurre en ocasiones al «principio de similitud». La Homeopatía lo hace sistemáticamente.

Los ejemplos comentados pueden aclarar la noción de los dos principios fundamentales de la Homeopatía: SIMILITUD y DOSIS INFINITESIMALES.

— La similitud consiste en administrar al paciente, justamente, la sustancia que es capaz de provocar unos **efectos semejantes** a los síntomas de su enfermedad.

— Pero esta sustancia deberá ser administrada en **dosis muy pequeñas**, totalmente atóxicas, pues en caso contrario agravaría el cuadro.

Materia médica homeopática

Patogenesias

omo ya hemos visto, Hahnemann observó que la administración de sustancias, en dosis no tóxicas, a individuos sanos, les provocaba una serie de síntomas que recogió con el nombre de **patogenesias**.

Los síntomas encontrados pueden ser **subjetivos** (percibidos únicamente por el sujeto y no por otras personas) y **objetivos** (fácilmente constatables por los demás), y aparecer a distintos niveles:

— **Local:** en una región concreta del organismo (hinchazón de un miembro, enrojecimiento de garganta, supuración de oídos, lengua sucia, etc., etc.).

— **General:** reacción de todo el organismo (cansancio, pérdida de apetito, fiebre, intolerancia al frío...).

— **Mental:** en la esfera psíquica (angustia, irratibilidad, miedo, tristeza, apatía...).

Naturalmente, desde Hahnemann, se han experimentado miles de sustancias, por lo que en la actualidad la Homeopatía cuenta con un enorme arsenal terapéutico.

El conjunto de todas las patogenesias constituye la «*Materia Médica Homeopática*», libro de texto imprescindible para todo homeópata, donde se recogen exhaustivamente todos los síntomas observados.

Origen de los medicamentos

Equivocadamente, se identifica la Homeopatía con una terapéutica mediante plantas. Aunque los materiales de los que se surte son naturales, no está restringida al reino vegetal, sino que emplea también elementos de origen animal y mineral.

Por otra parte, estas sustancias han de ser elaboradas de forma compleja, como más adelante veremos, siendo precisamente esta elaboración fundamental para conseguir el resultado deseado.

Cepas de origen vegetal

Se utilizan alrededor de 1.500 especies vegetales, de las que un 90 % son plantas salvajes recolectadas en su hábitat natural, donde presentan un óptimo estado. Factores como clima, terreno, altitud, ... influyen decisivamente en el producto final. Cuando la planta ha sido recolectada, se prepara con ella la «tintura madre», por maceración en solución hidroalcohólica, durante un mínimo de tres semanas.

Veamos algunos ejemplos de plantas utilizadas en Homeopatía, sus principios activos, efectos que producen y para qué se emplean.

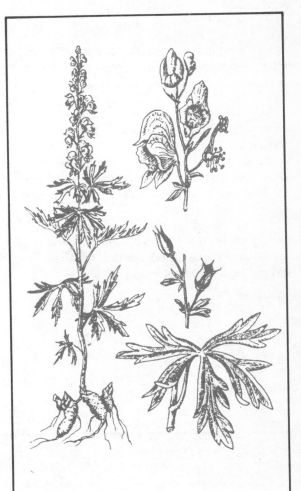

Aconitum napellus
Capuchón de monje o Carro de Venus

Crece en toda Europa. Se prepara la tintura madre con la planta entera, recogida hacia el fin de su floración (agosto).

Contiene algunos alcaloides sumamente tóxicos, como la aconitina y napellina, a los cuales debe sus principales propiedades.

Produce una triada característica con gran agitación, miedo a la muerte y fiebre alta, de aparición brusca.

En Homeopatía, es uno de los grandes remedios contra la fiebre.

Nux vomica

Crece en la India y norte de Australia, entre otros lugares. Tiene forma de arbusto, y la tintura se prepara a partir de las semillas de su fruto.

Sus principios activos son, entre otros, estricnina y brucina, alcaloides sumamente tóxicos.

Actúa a través del sistema nervioso central, produciendo una exagerada irritabilidad del mismo, con trastornos generalizados de tipo espasmódico.

Se usa frecuentemente por ser un remedio ideal para los efectos derivados del *stress* y abuso de tóxicos como alcohol, tabaco, exceso de medicaciones...

Arnica montana

Planta que crece en Europa Central En la preparación de la tintura se utiliza la raíz fresca.

Los responsables de sus efectos son dos glicósidos flavónicos: astragalina e isoquercetina.

Actúa sobre la piel, tejido celular subcutáneo, músculos y ligamentos, ocasionando dolores generalizados, «como si el cuerpo hubiese sido golpeado».

Es muy útil para el tratamiento de las molestias ocasionadas por traumatismos.

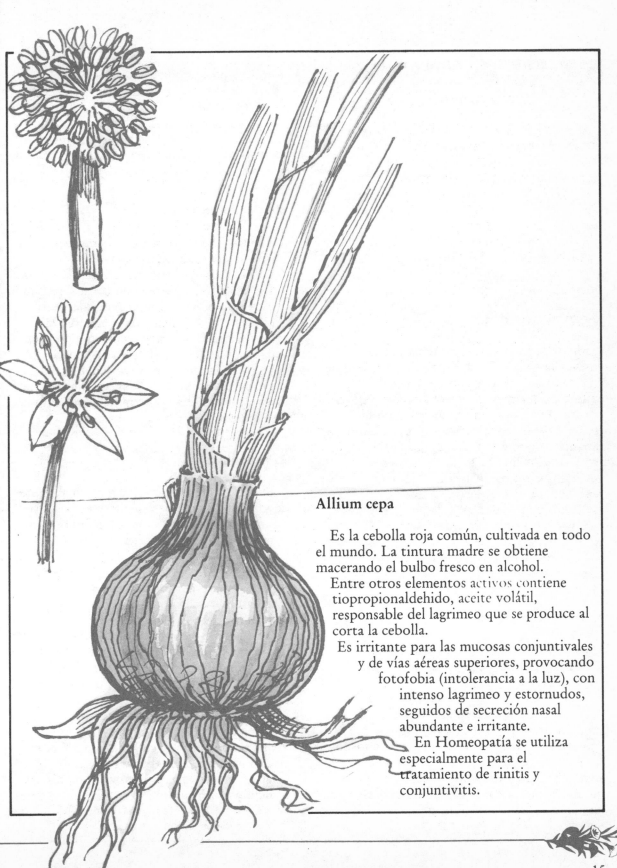

Allium cepa

Es la cebolla roja común, cultivada en todo el mundo. La tintura madre se obtiene macerando el bulbo fresco en alcohol.

Entre otros elementos activos contiene tiopropionaldehido, aceite volátil, responsable del lagrimeo que se produce al corta la cebolla.

Es irritante para las mucosas conjuntivales y de vías aéreas superiores, provocando fotofobia (intolerancia a la luz), con intenso lagrimeo y estornudos, seguidos de secreción nasal abundante e irritante.

En Homeopatía se utiliza especialmente para el tratamiento de rinitis y conjuntivitis.

Cepas de origen mineral

Son sales naturales, metales... seleccionados en el estado más puro posible.

Con los compuestos insolubles, no es factible la preparación directa de la tintura madre que se realizaba en el caso de los vegetales, por lo que, previamente, se procede a una trituración con lactosa en mortero, a partir de la cual se elaboran las diluciones homeopáticas.

Los minerales tienen efectos más profundos y duraderos sobre el organismo que los vegetales, cuya acción es, en general, más breve.

Cuprum metallicum

Metal de color rojo característico; se encuentra en la naturaleza, fundamentalmente en estado de pirita de cobre y asociado a sulfuros. El remedio homeopático se prepara triturando el cobre metálico precipitado.

Afecta al sistema nervioso, produciendo espasmos musculares, desde un simple temblor de dedos hasta convulsiones generalizadas o parálisis. En el plano sensitivo, causa en músculos, huesos, articulaciones y vísceras, calambres y dolores violentos que aparecen y desaparecen bruscamente.

El primer y principal uso homeopático de Cuprum son los calambres, espasmos musculares y convulsiones.

Natrum muriaticum

Es el cloruro sódico o sal marina. Se presenta en forma de cristales muy solubles en agua.

Sal importantísima en la constitución de nuestros tejidos, desempeña un papel fundamental en la difusión de líquidos a través de las membranas celulares, a todos los niveles. Así, en la sangre puede producir anemia por deformación y destrucción de los glóbulos rojos; en huesos, desmineralización; en mucosa, deshidratación, etc.

En general, afecta a todos los procesos de asimilación orgánica, pudiendo dar lugar a un estado de depresión física y mental, con debilidad generalizada.

Tiene una enorme variedad de aplicaciones, algunas de las cuales pueden ser anemias, trastornos del desarrollo de los niños, falta de apetito, desnutrición e hipotensión.

Mercurius corrosivus

Es una sal de mercurio que se presenta en forma de pequeñas masas cristalinas incoloras, de sabor metálico muy desagradable.

Da lugar a ulceraciones en córnea, garganta, genitales..., que se extienden rápidamente y producen dolores ardientes y agudos. Hay diarrea disenteriforme y tenesmo intenso de vejiga y recto, es decir, deseo continuo, doloroso e ineficaz de orinar y defecar.

Es, precisamente, en estas lesiones de tipo ulcerativo y en diarreas con tenesmo, donde este remedio encuentra su aplicación.

Arsenicum album

El anhídrido arsenioso, el más importante de los compuestos de arsénico, se encuentra raramente en forma pura, obteniéndose por combustión de otros minerales con los que está combinado.

Su administración de forma aguda produce efectos digestivos, como náuseas, vómitos y diarreas; fuertes dolores de cabeza y sed intensa. Si la dosis es tóxica, se llega al colapso, con deposiciones abundantes y líquidas, coléricas o sanguinolentas y destrucción de los glóbulos rojos. Si la administración es prolongada, desemboca en caquexia (alteración grave de la nutrición), con trastornos respiratorios y erupciones secas y descamantes de la piel.

Su esfera de acción en Homeopatía es muy amplia: se emplea en el tratamiento de diarreas, afecciones respiratorias con disnea (dificultad para respirar), erupciones cutáneas, fiebre, etc.

Cepas de origen animal

Los más utilizados como remedios homeopáticos de esta procedencia, son insectos triturados (abejas, hormigas, arañas...), venenos y secreciones de diversos animales, que constituyen medios terapéuticos muy potentes.

Dos ejemplos característicos pueden ser:

Apis mellifica

Es la abeja común, triturada en lactosa.

Todos sabemos cuáles son los síntomas propios de una picadura de abeja: tumefacción de la zona, que se encuentra caliente, con enrojecimiento y dolor «picante» y ardiente, que se alivia con aplicaciones frías y empeora con el tacto y la presión.

Fácilmente se deducirá su aplicación en quemaduras solares, fiebre, algunos reumatismos inflamatorios y, en general, en todos los cuadros que tengan los síntomas mencionados.

Lachesis

Es el veneno del Lachesis Trigonocephalus, gran serpiente, extremadamente venenosa, de América del Sur.

La picadura del animal produce localmente una gran inflamación, muy dolorosa, con manchas azuladas cubiertas de vesículas sanguinolentas, que puede terminar en ulceración gangrenosa.

Actúa rápidamente sobre centros nerviosos y sangre, que pierde la propiedad de coagularse, dando lugar a hemorragias.

Algunas de sus indicaciones son enfermedades con alteraciones de la coagulación sanguínea y afecciones graves y tórpidas de la piel.

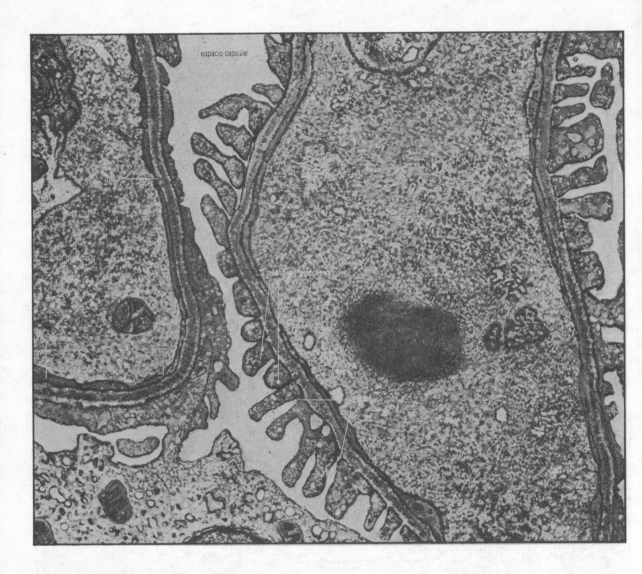

espacio capsular

Glomérulo renal. Los extractos de los tejidos renales son la base de técnicas homeopáticas.

Sustancias de origen microbiano

La llamada «Bioterapia» utiliza medicamentos preparados a partir de productos de origen microbiano (cultivos, sueros o vacunas) o de secreciones patológicas, que se emplean, en virtud de una analogía causal, para tratar un cuadro infeccioso o una predisposición individual a padecer ciertas enfermedades.

Dentro de este subgrupo están las cepas de origen isoterápico, que se obtienen a partir de tomas biológicas del propio enfermo —sangre, saliva, descamaciones...

Cepas organoterápicas

Son extractos glandulares y tisulares (tiroides, riñón, hipófisis, suprarrenales...) preparados con técnicas homeopáticas.

No se trata de una terapéutica sustitutiva, ya que las dosis empleadas son infinitesimales, sino reaccional, es decir que estimula o frena al tejido o glándula enfermos, restableciendo la función alterada.

Preparación del medicamento homeopático

El procedimiento de fabricación del medicamento homeopático se lleva a cabo siguiendo fielmente las instrucciones de Hahnemann, con la ventaja de que actualmente se realiza en laboratorios especializados, con medios técnicos muy sofisticados y un riguroso control de calidad, que otorgan la mayor fiabilidad al producto final.

Obtención de la tintura madre

La preparación inicial del remedio depende de su procedencia, de forma que las sustancias solubles pueden macerarse directamente en el disolvente, mientras que las insolubles necesitan otros procedimientos intermedios.

El disolvente más eficaz es el alcohol o una mezcla de éste con agua, debido a sus propiedades. El alcohol es el principal disolvente de los compuestos orgánicos y permite la extracción de sustancias activas de plantas y materias animales, así como de algunos minerales tras su trituración. El agua diluye gran cantidad de minerales como las sales y los hidróxidos; por el contrario, es un

mal disolvente de materias orgánicas, papel que deja al alcohol.

Los vegetales y elementos de origen animal se maceran en una solución de alcohol de 65-70° o alcohol-agua, durante un tiempo mínimo de 21 días, al cabo del cual, por filtrado, obtenemos la Tintura Madre (T.M.), que posee una elevada concentración del producto inicial: para lograr un solo kilo de T.M. son necesarios 10 kilos de plantas deshidratadas y 20 kilos de productos animales.

Dilución y dinamización

Una vez obtenida la Tintura Madre, comienza el peculiar proceso de preparación del medicamento homeopático, que consiste en ir disminuyendo la cantidad de principio activo de manera progresiva, lo que trae consigo la atenuación, o incluso la anulación total, del efecto tóxico de la sustancia inicial. Pero, con esto, nos limitaríamos únicamente a realizar disminuciones de concentración del producto original. Es necesario, por tanto, un proceso que, realizado entre cada dilución, confiere a ésta unas propiedades particulares que caracterizan al medicamento homeopático: se trata de la DINAMIZACION, que consiste en agitar enérgicamente el frasco de vidrio que contiene la sustancia diluida.

Hahnemann realizaba la dinamización rudimentariamente, sacudiendo los frascos sobre un libro con tapas de cuero. En nuestros días, los laboratorios cuentan con «dinamizadores», máquinas especialmente diseñadas para este fin.

Este sería el proceso en conjunto:
Tomaremos 1 cc. de Tintura Madre y lo añadiremos a 99 c.c. del disolvente. Después de agitar enérgicamente, habremos conseguido la «1.ª dilución centesimal hahnemaniana» (1 CH). Si de ésta se toma 1 c.c. y se lleva a 99 c.c. de disolvente se obtiene, tras la respectiva dinamización, la 2 CH y así sucesivamente.

Por supuesto, de la misma forma que se realizan las diluciones centesimales, en 100 c.c., se pueden elaborar otras decimales, en 10 c.c.: llevando una parte de T.M. a 9 de solvente resultaría la 1 DH...

Estos es fácilmente comprensible cuando partimos de una Tintura Madre, pero en el caso de los minerales no solubles habrá que seguir un procedimiento intermedio: la trituración. Con ella vamos a conseguir disminuir la concentración de la sustancia inicial y, por otra parte, reducirla a partículas tan pequeñísimas que puedan disolverse en un medio líquido, como ocurría en el caso de animales y vegetales. ¿Cómo logramos ambos fines?:

Si trituramos en un mortero una parte de mineral con 99 de un elemento inerte como la lactosa, conseguiremos la 1 CH; una parte de este producto con 99 de lactosa, nos darán la

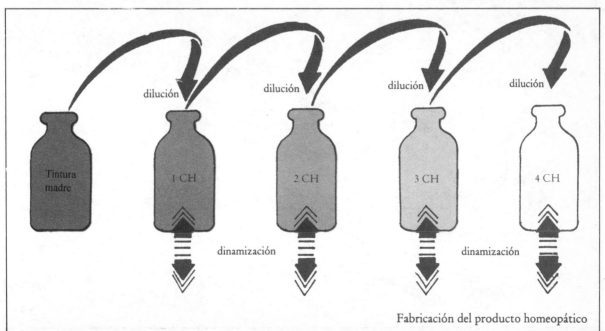

Fabricación del producto homeopático

2 CH. A partir de la 3 CH la sustancia, en principio insoluble, deja de serlo, y las desconcentraciones posteriores podrán realizarse directamente por dilución, de la forma ya comentada.

Formas de presentación

El proceso que hemos descrito en los párrafos precedentes, da como resultado lo que se podría llamar «materia prima» para la elaboración final del medicamento homeopático. Las diluciones obtenidas no son más que dosis decrecientes de la sustancia original, y con ellas se preparan las distintas formas de presentación del remedio, tal como lo podemos encontrar en las farmacias: gránulos y glóbulos (pequeñas esferas de sacarosa y lactosa, impregnadas con el principio activo), gotas, ampollas bebibles e inyectables, pomadas y supositorios.

Algunos experimentos de interés

La investigación en Homeopatía comenzó con Hahnemann, que experimentó la acción de escasas dosis de las principales sustancias empleadas en su época como medicamentos, para mostrar la validez de la Ley de Semejanzas.

Desde entonces, los homeópatas han continuado realizando numerosos trabajos científicos para probar la utilidad del empleo del similar a pequeñas dosis. En los últimos treinta años, la investigación ha mostrado de manera mensurable y reproductible la acción de las diluciones infinitesimales en animales de laboratorio y vegetales.

Los resultados obtenidos han permitido la oficialización de la Homeopatía en Francia, por su introducción en la Farmacopea en 1965.

Se ha dicho en contra de la Homeopatía, que las respuestas conseguidas eran debidas

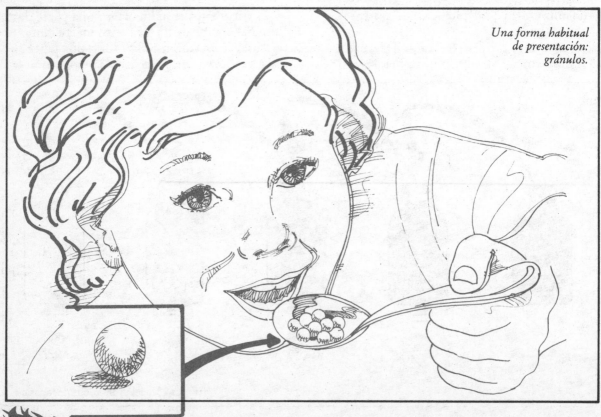

Una forma habitual de presentación: gránulos.

únicamente al llamado «efecto placebo» (placebo es un preparado inerte que se prescribe para lograr un efecto psicoterápico). No se puede negar el efecto placebo que posee cualquier tipo de medicación, tanto alopática como homeopática, e incluso se lo podría atribuir al mismo médico, ya que después de que éste infunde confianza en sus pacientes, éstos mejoran aun sin tratamiento.

Sin embargo, los notables éxitos, alcanzados mediante remedios homeopáticos en animales —la Homeopatía se utiliza cada vez con mayor frecuencia en veterinaria— y en plantas, invalidan la explicación del efecto placebo del medicamento.

Sería tedioso describir en esta rápida exposición la multitud de investigaciones efectuadas, así que nos limitaremos a seleccionar algunas representativas:

— El aloxano es una sustancia que tiene la propiedad de provocar una diabetes experimental cuando se inyecta a ratones o ratas, es decir, un aumento de glucosa en sangre por degeneración de las células pancreáticas productoras de insulina.

Si se inyecta aloxano a un primer grupo de ratones a dosis de 40 mg. por kilo de peso, al cabo de 4 ó 5 días se puede comprobar que las cifras de glucosa en sangre han aumentado mucho y el animal puede llegar a morir por diabetes.

Si a un segundo grupo de ratones se administra, durante 6 días consecutivos, aloxano diluido homeopáticamente a la 9 CH, antes de inyectar la mencionada dosis tóxica, se observa que estos animales no presentan aumento de glucosa en sangre: no llegan a estar diabéticos. **Han sido protegidos** por las diluciones homeopáticas de aloxano.

Asimismo, se han realizado tratamientos curativos de la diabetes en animales por medio de Aloxano 9 CH.

— Es posible provocar hepatitis experimentales en la rata, por administración de tetracloruro de carbono. Pues bien, se ha demostrado que estas hepatitis podían ser tratadas preventivamente o curadas por disoluciones homeopáticas de Phosphorus 15 CH —que en dosis tóxicas produce una hepatitis muy similar a la del tetracloruro de carbono—, resultados objetivados por análisis y observación del tejido hepático al microscopio.

— Si a un cobaya con eritema (enrojecimiento de la piel) por exposición prolongada a rayos ultravioleta, se le administra Apis Mellífica 7 CH —es el veneno de abeja, que en dosis mayores da lugar a síntomas muy parecidos a las quemaduras solares— se comprueba una protección contra la inflamación de hasta el 80 % a las 24 horas.

Si tenemos en cuenta que serían necesarias dosis altas de antiinflamatorios clásicos, con el ácido salicílico, fenilbutazona, indometacina, hidrocortisona... entre otros, para conseguir una protección del 50 %, queda reflejada la efectividad de este remedio homeopático.

— Por fin, veamos brevemente el efecto de disoluciones homeopáticas de Histaminum sobre la respuesta alérgica, por medio del llamado «test de degranulación de los basófilos».

Los basófilos son glóbulos blancos normalmente presentes en la sangre, que contienen gránulos con una sustancia llamada histamina. En caso de que el individuo se ponga en contacto con una sustancia capaz de producir alergia, esta histamina será liberada a la sangre, dando lugar a las desagradables manifestaciones propias de los cuadros alérgicos.

Si previamente al contacto con la sustancia sensibilizante se administran diluciones de Histaminun 5 CH, se bloqueará totalmente, en un 76 % de los casos, la liberación de los gránulos de histamina.

Estos y otros muchos trabajos muestran de manera significativa, reproductible y estadísticamente valedera, la actividad de las disoluciones homeopáticas.

Terreno constitucional y clasificación de las enfermedades

s indudable, y cada días se va comprendiendo más, que la persona reacciona siempre en su totalidad, como una unidad indisoluble. No se pueden hacer separaciones artificiales entre enfermedades físicas y psíquicas, ya que la enfermedad, cualquiera que sea su asiento, constituye una alteración en el equilibrio fisio-psicológico que es el individuo.

La Medicina clínica analítica, que caracterizó la investigación científica desde el siglo XIX hasta nuestros días, ha fijado su atención predominantemente en las causas y síntomas de las enfermedades, olvidando que la lesión anatómica no es la enfermedad, sino su consecuencia, y dejando a un lado la visión del paciente en su conjunto y de su alteración, como un intento de adaptación del organismo a circunstancias adversas.

Algunas escuelas, a lo largo de la historia, preconizan la comprensión global del individuo. Centrándonos en la Medicina Occidental, ya que la Oriental desde sus orígenes hasta hoy no ha perdido de vista este concepto, se observa que ya la Escuela Hipocrática considera que no se debe tratar únicamente la parte enferma, sin recordar que pertenece a un todo que puede condicionar decisivamente la eficacia terapéutica.

Distingue dos grandes grupos de causas productoras de enfermedades: externas (mala alimentación, agresiones térmicas, traumatismos...) e internas (raza, sexo y TEMPERAMENTO). Creen que el estado de salud depende del equilibrio entre cuatro humores básicos: sangre, flema, bilis amarilla y bilis negra o melancolía.

Sobre el esquema humoral hipocrático, Galeno construye su célebre tipología del temperamento, que aún perdura, clasificando a los individuos en sanguíneos, flemáticos o linfáticos, coléricos o biliosos y melancólicos. Según Galeno, «la causa externa sólo produce enfermedad cuando actúa sobre un individuo que, por obra de su constitución, es morbosamente sensible a ella. La misma causa externa puede hacer enfermar a unos y deja indemnes a otros». Por tanto, esta especial constitución sería la causa interna que colabora en la producción de la enfermedad.

D. Quijote es un buen ejemplo de leptosomáticos: largo, delgado, idealista, vive en su propio mundo.

Sancho Panza es el arquetipo del pícnico: buen comedor y bebedor, realista, eminentemente práctico, sociable.

La Medicina Occidental no concede valor a la conexión de la morfología del sujeto con su psico-fisiología, sino hasta principios del siglo XX, en que se vuelve a dar importancia a la relación entre la constitución individual y la disposición o resistencia a la enfermedad. Son varios los autores que elaboran teorías respecto a esto, siendo el más significativo Kretschmer, que define tres biotipos o grupos de individuos que poseen la misma constitución hereditaria fundamental: pícnico, leptosomático y atlético, atribuyendo a cada uno de ellos una predisposición a padecer ciertas enfermedades psíquicas y físicas. Así, el individuo «pícnico», con tórax y cuello anchos y cortos, tiene, psicológicamente, una tendencia a la alternancia entre manía (exaltación del tono afectivo) y depresión, y está más predispuesto que otros a enfermedades cardiovasculares —hipertensión arterial, alteraciones coronarias...—; por el contrario, el «leptosomático», sujeto con miembros largos y tórax estrecho, tiene tendencia a la esquizofrenia y a enfermedades como tuberculosis, úlcera gastroduodenal...

Cervantes ilustra de manera increíblemente clara estos dos biotipos, de forma que D. Quijote es un buen ejemplo del leptosomático (largo, delgado, idealista, vive en su propio mundo...), y Sancho Panza lo es del pícnico (buen comedor y bebedor, realista, eminentemente práctico, sociable...).

Aunque a lo largo de la historia se han hecho tentativas para formular un diagnóstico constitucional, ninguno es tan completo y detallado como el homeopático.

La Homeopatía, al realizar sus patogenesias experimentales y con el agregado de la observación clínica, ha construido unos cuadros constitucionales completísimos, formados por un conjunto de síntomas psíquicos y físicos, encontrados en sujetos con una determinada morfología.

Para explicar esto más claramente, hemos seleccionado un remedio, entre tantos otros constitucionales como podemos encontrar en la Materia Médica:

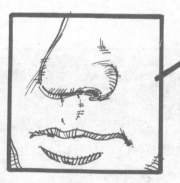

Somnolencia durante el día y gran debilidad ante cualquier esfuerzo.

Propensión a resfriarse fácilmente ante la menor corriente de aire.

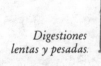

Digestiones lentas y pesadas.

*Sujeto
característico
«Calcárea Carbónica»,
piel blanca, rubio, ojos claros,
tendencia a la obesidad; friolero, lento,
apático, melancólico.*

Calcarea Carbonica

— El sujeto característico es gordo o con tendencia a la obesidad, con piel muy blanca, rubio, de ojos claros.

— Mientras el sistema óseo tiene un desarrollo irregular y tardío, las partes blandas crecen en exceso, de donde proviene su tendencia a la obesidad y al aumento de tamaño de los ganglios y amígdalas.

— Suda con facilidad, fundamentalmente por ciertas regiones, como la cabeza.

— Es extremedamente friolero.

— Marcada disposición a la apatía, con lentitud ante todo esfuerzo físico o mental.

— Los niños son de abdomen globuloso y cabeza grande. Tienen, en general, un retardo en el crecimiento, con dentición atrasada y mala calcificación de los huesos, lo que produce tendencia a su incurvación. Tienen predisposición a la anemia.

Un individuo como el descrito puede manifestar unos síntomas característicos:

— **Cabeza:**
Cefaleas congestivas, con sensación de frío externo intenso en diferentes partes de la cabeza.
Vértigo giratorio con pérdida del equilibrio.

— **Aparato digestivo:**
Faringitis con sensación de sequedad y constricción al tragar.
Digestiones lentas y pesadas, con hinchazón, plenitud y eructos agrios.
Estómago distendido y sensible.
Rechaza la leche y la grasa y prefiere de forma especial los huevos.
Alternancia de estreñimiento y diarreas ácidas.

— **Aparato respiratorio:**
Propensión a resfriarse fácilmente, ante la menor corriente de aire.
Ronquera crónica.

— **Aparato génito urinario:**
En la mujer, menstruación adelantada, larga y abundante, acompañada de mucho frío.

En el hombre, deseos sexuales aumentados, con problemas en la erección y eyaculación.

— **Aparato circulatorio:**
Palpitaciones después del menor ejercicio.
Pulso acelerado y débil.

— **Espalda y extremidades:**
Desviación de columna vertebral, con dolores a distintos niveles (entre los hombros, tortícolis, lumbago...).
Entumecimiento general.
Pies fríos y húmedos, «como si tuviera puestas medias húmedas».
Marcha tardía en los niños, por debilidad ósea.

— **Piel:**
Eczema húmedo en cuero cabelludo, formando costras espesas y blanquecinas.

— **Sueño:**
Somnolencia durante el día, sobre todo después de cenar. Desea acostarse temprano, pero durante la noche despierta con frecuencia o tiene insomnio y pesadillas.
Se levanta agotado por la mañana.

— **Psiquismo:**
Gran debilidad ante cualquier esfuerzo intelectual, con fatiga rápida y dificultad para fijar la atención.
Melancolía, tristeza, depresión. Tendencia irresistible a llorar; al mismo tiempo puede estar irritable, impaciente e incluso tener accesos de cólera.
Preocupación por detalles insignificantes, por cosas sin importancia.

— **Modalidades:**
Todos los síntomas empeoran por el frío y por trabajo, ya sea físico o intelectual, y mejoran con el tiempo seco y cálido.
Hay predominio de las alteraciones en el lado derecho del cuerpo.

Este ejemplo ilustra la exhaustiva descripción que realiza la Homeopatía en sus remedios constitucionales.

Por lo tanto, estudiando las características de ciertos medicamentos homeopáticos

(Lycopodium, Sulphur, Silicea, Natrum Muriaticum, Phosphorus, etc., etc.), se obtiene una visión sintética de los biotipos constitucionales.

Cuando en un paciente logramos encontrar todas las características esenciales que constan en un remedio concreto, decimos de ese remedio que es el SIMILIMUM del enfermo y constituye el **tratamiento ideal** en las **enfermedades crónicas**, pues pondrá en marcha la reacción curativa de todo el organismo.

Enfermedades agudas y crónicas

Tradicionalmente, se han venido distinguiendo dos formas de evolución de la enfermedad: aguda y crónica.

Para la Medicina Clásica, la diferencia entre ambas se basa fundamentalmente en la duración del proceso en el tiempo; así, enfermedad aguda sería aquella de aparición brusca y corta duración, en una persona presumiblemente sana, que evoluciona hacia la resolución, ya sea la curación o la muerte, si la enfermedad es grave. Por el contrario, la crónica sería aquella de más larga duración (meses, años, a veces toda la vida).

Cuando una enfermedad aguda no tiende a finalizar, se dice que «se ha cronificado», dando de esta forma la importancia primordial al **tiempo de evolución.**

Pero la Homeopatía tiene un criterio más amplio para clasificar las enfermedades, de forma que no sólo tiene en cuenta su duración, sino más bien su **naturaleza.** Así, se considera también enfermedad crónica a aquella que tiende a continuar en el paciente, manifestándose en distintas formas, **una después de otra.**

Pongamos, por ejemplo, un niño gordito, con tendencia a la anemia y mala calcificación de los huesos, que padeció un eczema húmedo de cuero cabelludo en su primera infancia y ahora presenta resfriados muy frecuentes, provocados por la menor corriente de aire. Aunque, aparentemente, todos estos son episodios aislados, sin conexión alguna, para el médico homeópata constituyen manifestaciones de una misma enfermedad crónica, que asienta sobre un terreno constitucional concreto: Calcarea Carbonica, en este caso.

Es el terreno el que hace que una enfermedad, que pudo aparecer como aguda y cesar después, tienda a continuar en el mismo paciente bajo otra forma. Se tratará, en este caso, de distintas manifestaciones de una enfermedad crónica de base.

Veamos otro caso en el que, un episodio aparentemente agudo, no es más que la presentación de una tendencia crónica a enfermar:

Una crisis de diarrea provocada por ingestión de verduras, podría ser considerada como aguda si fuera un hecho aislado en la vida del sujeto, pero si siempre que esta persona come verduras tiene diarrea, no se puede tomar como una crisis aguda aislada, sino que, en este caso, la diarrea manifiesta un desequilibrio del terreno constitucional de este individuo.

Para el tratamiento de las enfermedades crónicas, se ha de intentar encontrar el medicamento que cubra la totalidad de las características esenciales del paciente que es, como ya se refirió anteriormente, el SIMILIMUM.

En las enfermedades agudas, es suficiente con administrar aquel remedio que abarque los síntomas que presenta el paciente en ese momento, que pueden ser exclusivamente locales (dolor de garganta), o acompañarse de reacciones generales (fiebre) y mentales (agitación). Todos los síntomas han de recogerse con sus modalidades de agravación y mejoría, como se indica en el siguiente capítulo, para poder delimitar claramente un remedio concreto de entre todos los posibles.

Historia clínica homeopática: «retrato del paciente»

a historia clínica es el conjunto de datos subjetivos (aportados por el propio paciente) y objetivos (exploración, análisis, radiografías...), en los que se basa el médico para establecer un diagnóstico e instaurar posteriormente el tratamiento oportuno.

En una primera fase, la historia clínica homeopática no se diferencia sustancialmente de la habitual en Medicina clásica. Por medio de un correcto interrogatorio, se recogen los síntomas que motivan la consulta del paciente, además del funcionamiento subjetivo de la totalidad de órganos y aparatos, así como las enfermedades padecidas en el pasado, propias y familiares, dando especial importancia a las que se presentan de forma repetitiva (se ven con frecuencia familias con tendencia a determinadas enfermedades como diabetes, alteraciones cardiovasculares, tumores...).

Al interrogatorio se añade una exploración física y una serie de pruebas complementarias (análisis, radiografías...), con todo lo cual se

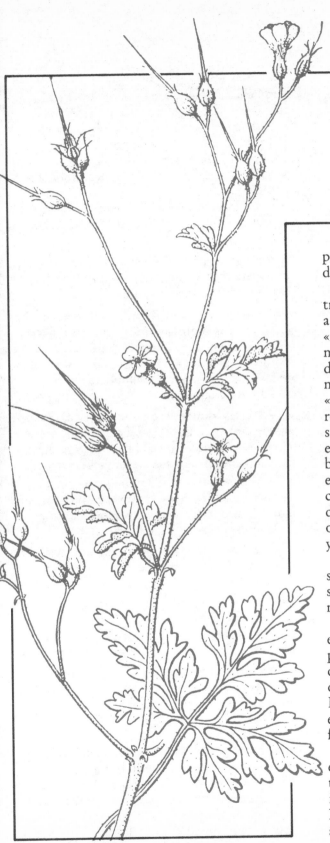

El remedio homeopático Gelsemium no se prepara con la especie que crece en Europa sino con una originaria de Norteamérica, con cuyo rizoma se hace la tintura.

puede llegar a un diagnóstico bastante preciso de la **enfermedad** que presenta el sujeto.

En este punto terminaría la historia clínica tradicional. Pero la Homeopatía no se limita a conocer el nombre de la enfermedad, ya que «no hay enfermedades sino enfermos», pues a menudo vemos que dos personas reaccionan de manera diferente y característica ante una misma patología. Hahnemann, en su libro *«Organon del Arte de curar»*, observa: «Con respecto a la investigación del total de síntomas, es enteramente indiferente que haya existido jamás algo semejante en el mundo, bajo cualquier nombre que sea. Durante el examen de un caso, hay que olvidarse de cualquier otro que haya sido similar. Nunca deberíamos sustituir por hipótesis la observación, nunca considerar un caso como ya conocido.»

La misma escuela hipocrática evitaba siempre dar un diagnóstico preestablecido, y se limitaba a describir los síntomas en el momento de tratar un paciente.

Para la Homeopatía, la enfermedad no existe como entidad abstracta fuera de la persona. El enfermo es visto como un todo, de forma que su estado actual es inseparable de su pasado personal y hereditario.
La enfermedad es un episodio integrado en la historia general del individuo y su familia biológica.

La historia completa del paciente es, pues, el único diagnóstico que el enfermo tiene, y a través de ella se puede conocer como individuo único, irrepetible y determinado
Por tanto, los hechos que nos revelan al sujeto «como enfermo, no como enfermedad»

son los que constituyen la parte más característica de la historia clínica homeopática. Esta ha de hacerse de forma minuciosa, recogiendo gran cantidad de datos, por lo que tiene que ser realizada sin condicionamientos de tiempo. La primera consulta requiere no menos de una hora, en la cual el paciente hace un relato ESPONTANEO de lo que le sucede. Esto quiere decir que el médico no debe dirigir las respuestas, sino únicamente reflejar todo lo que el enfermo le proporcione, concediendo especial importancia a signos y síntomas, curiosos en ocasiones, y que habitualmente se tiende a desestimar. Así, vemos con frecuencia en la consulta, pacientes que anteceden sus explicaciones con la frase «doctor, va a reírse usted si le digo lo que he observado...». Sin embargo, estas palabras suelen ser el preludio de datos significativos para nosotros. Veamos un ejemplo: si una persona consultara por un dolor de cabeza de tipo congestivo, con sensación de latidos, especialmente en la nuca y acompañado de náuseas y vómitos, tendríamos una amplia gama de remedios que podrían aliviarle; pero cuando el enfermo refiere que sus molestias mejoran después de orinar abundantemente, nos está orientando hacia un remedio concreto: GELSEMIUM.

Por tanto, ningún síntoma, por extraño o absurdo que parezca, debe, al menos en principio, ser despreciado.

Sería muy extenso presentar todos los datos que nos puede aportar un paciente, por ello recogemos a continuación algunos puntos que nos interesa conocer:

— **Alimentación:** Se debe interrogar no sólo sobre si el sujeto tiene o no buen apetito, sino también sobre sus gustos peculiares: ¿qué alimentos o sabores desea especialmente?, ¿cuáles le desagradan de manera particular?, ¿hay alimentos que, aún gustándole, le sientan mal?...

— **Sed:** Ausente o muy intensa; insaciable o fácil de calmar; de líquidos fríos o calientes; dentro o fuera de las comidas; síntomas contradictorios como «boca seca, sin sed»...

— **Ritmo intestinal:** * estreñimiento con ausencia de deseo para defecar, con deseos ineficaces, defecación costosa e incompleta...

* diarrea: violenta, irritante, en chorro, dolorosa o no, provocada por ciertos estímulos (alimentación, nerviosismo...), seguida de gran postración, con sudoración profusa...;

* alternancia de estreñimiento y diarrea o aspectos disímiles de las evacuaciones...

— **Sudoración:** excesiva o escasa; olor de la misma; localizada en regiones particulares; circunstancias que la provocan; ¿mejoran otros síntomas cuando suda?...

— **Menstruación** abundante o escasa; con ciclos cortos o prolongados; características del flujo menstrual (color, coágulos...); dolorosa o no. Es importante saber sin con la menstruación mejoran o empeoran otros síntomas de la paciente.

— **Actividad:** Persona muy activa, que no puede estar quieta o, por el contrario, prefiere el reposo; cómo influye el movimiento en su estado general o en sus afecciones concretas...

— **Posición:** Ver si hay mejoría o agravación de ciertos síntomas en relación a la postura adoptada (acostado sobre uno u otro lado, con la cabeza baja, de pie...).

— **Sexualidad:** Deseo sexual aumentado o disminuido; problemas en el coito (rechazo, coito doloroso...).

— **Sueño:** Ligero, muy profundo, sobresaltado; insomnio, sonambulismo, pesadillas. Qué postura adopta el sujeto para dormir. Cómo se encuentra al despertar...

— **Reacción general del organismo ante:**

* Horario: momentos del día en los que el enfermo se encuentra mejor y peor, física y psíquicamente.

* Temperatura y clima: se trata de conocer si el individuo es friolero o caluroso, tiene preferencias por algún clima determinado y sus reacciones ante humedad, aire libre, exposición al sol, tormentas, cambios de tiempo..., así como ante aplicaciones de calor y frío local.

*El remedio homeopático Bryonia
se prepara tanto con la nueza roja
tratada en la ilustración como con la
blanca, Bryonia dioica y Bryonia alba respectivamente*

— **Lateralidad:** Predominio de las alteraciones en el lado derecho o izquierdo del cuerpo.

— **Es necesario investigar:** Si existe periodicidad en los síntomas, es decir, si éstos se producen cada cierto tiempo fijo; si hay alternancia entre distintas afecciones (estreñimiento-diarrea; apetito-inapetencia; eczema-asma; eczema-coriza; celafea-trastornos digestivos, etc.) y si están provocadas por causas concretas (sustos, frío, alimentación, baño...).

Hemos dejado para el final la parte esencial de la historia clínica: los llamados «síntomas mentales». No se puede considerar al enfermo como un organismo mecánico; lo psíquico constituye la más elevada función biológica. La realidad clínica exige que el médico tenga una visión total del sujeto para llegar a comprenderle en su funcionamiento como persona. Por todo ello los pacientes deben ser estudiados en el trasfondo de su personalidad, la forma en que ésta se manifiesta, su actitud vital frente al trabajo, familia y sociedad en general.

Muchos de los síntomas mentales se pueden observar a través de la actitud del paciente (locuacidad, minuciosidad, orden, concentración, etc.); otros se obtendrán por medio del interrogatorio. Investigaremos cuál es su postura ante la vida, cómo se relaciona con el medio —familia, trabajo, amigos, sociedad—; los cambios en el estado de ánimo —tristeza y alegría repentina, irritabilidad—, llanto y reacción ante el consuelo, son hechos importantes. Deben ser tomados seriamente en consideración los temores, ideas fijas, manías. ¿Tiene nuestro paciente dificultades para concentrarse o memorizar? ¿Insiste excesivamente en detalles secundarios como limpieza, puntualidad, orden?...

El ser vivo es una unidad psico-biológica, por lo que, para la curación, es necesario tener en cuenta la totalidad de los síntomas, no sólo los que constituye el cuadro actual, sino su actitud vital psicológica que confiere sentido a su proceso de enfermar.

Hemos recogido, hasta aquí, síntomas diversos (locales, generales y mentales), pero en Homeopatía, un síntoma aislado no tiene valor si no es «MODALIZADO». La modalización le confiere unas características particulares que le dan individualidad, que hacen que deje de ser común. De esta forma, un paciente con dolores de tipo reumático que empeoran al moverse y mejoran con reposo y acostándose sobre la región dolorida, requeriría como medicamento «Bryonia». Pero si ocurriera a la inversa, es decir, que este dolor mejorara por el movimiento, agravándose en reposo y acostado sobre el lado doloroso, el tratamiento sería distinto: «Rhus Toxicodendron».

El síntoma «tos», sin más características, no es valorable, pero sí lo es cuando se le modaliza:«tos que empeora estando al aire libre».

Por tanto, un síntoma adquiere significación si se conoce una serie de datos sobre él: mejorías o agravaciones ante determinadas circunstancias o estímulos, horario de aparición, influencia del clima, lateralidad predominante, etc.

Por otra parte no todos los síntomas recogidos tienen el mismo valor, aunque estén modalizados. Hay que hacer una escala de prioridades, concediendo mayor importancia a:

— Los síntomas **mentales** característicos, que tienen mayor valor en el momento de la prescripción, fundamentalmente en el tratamiento de enfermedades crónicas y del terreno constitucional.

— Síntomas relatados **espontáneamente** por el enfermo.

— Síntomas **atípicos, peculiares:** es más extraño encontrar «fiebre de 40° C sin sed» que con ella. Del mismo modo es más curioso un dolor que mejora por la presión fuerte, que otro con intolerancia a ella.

De esta manera, sabemos mucho más que el nombre de la enfermedad que aqueja al paciente; conocemos también cómo vive su dolencia, cómo reacciona ante ella y cómo ha llegado a padecerla. Hemos conseguido INDIVIDUALIZAR totalmente al enfermo, obteniendo un auténtico retrato de él.

Prescripción homeopática

Elección del medicamento

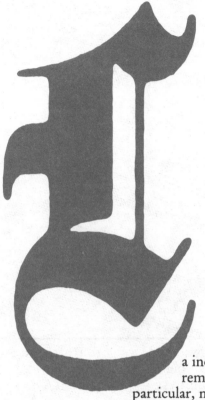

La individualización y selección del remedio, aplicado a cada caso en particular, no representan grandes dificultades, porque el enfermo los lleva en sí mismo, exactamente revelados por sus síntomas. Estas manifestaciones sintomáticas características debe buscarlas el médico y las encontrará en la forma de trastornos «psíquicos», «sensoriales», «funcionales» y «lesionales».

Para elegir el medicamento adecuado en Homeopatía, hay que establecer una relación analógica entre el conjunto de síntomas presentado por el enfermo y el grupo de síntomas que provoca un determinado remedio. Cuanto mayor sea la superposición entre el «retrato clínico» obtenido del paciente y el «retrato medicamentoso», la efectividad terapéutica también será mayor.

Si un sujeto consultara por problemas digestivos de distensión y pesadez abdominal, con necesidad de aflojarse la ropa después de las comidas e hipersensibilidad al presionar el

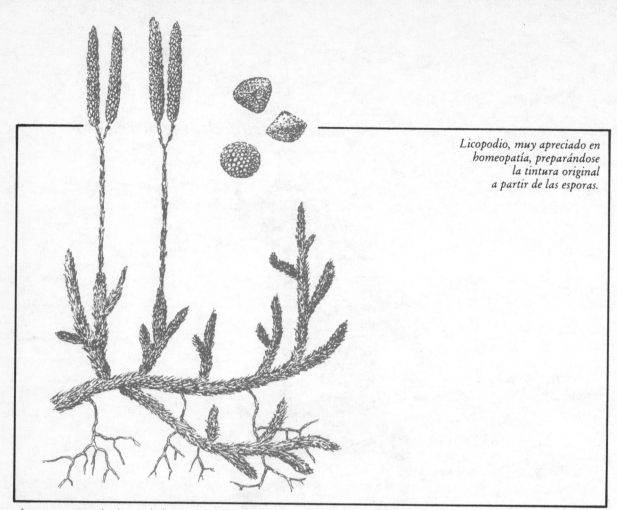

Licopodio, muy apreciado en homeopatía, preparándose la tintura original a partir de las esporas.

vientre, estreñimiento y hemorroides, podría ser aliviado por varios medicamentos que poseen síntomas digestivos muy similares: Kali Carbonicum, Lycopodium, Nux Vomica, Carbo Vegetabilis, Sepia, Sulphur... Pero, si además sabemos que se trata de un individuo muy activo, con exceso de trabajo mental, irritable e intolerante, con hábitos sedentarios y que abusa de café, tabaco y alcohol, clarísimamente la indicación se concreta en Nux Vomica, remedio que, además de los mencionados síntomas digestivos, abarca también el psiquismo de este enfermo. Habremos encontrado el remedio más semejante a nuestro paciente, que logrará su curación.

Sin embargo, por diversas causas —síntomas imprecisos, cuadros muy complejos, modalidades contradictorias...— no siempre es posible tratar un enfermo con un único remedio, por lo que en la práctica es necesario, en ocasiones, utilizar varios.

En este sentido existen distintas corrientes en Homeopatía:

Unicistas: Preconizan la utilización de un solo remedio, que abarque íntegramente al paciente.

Pluralistas: Los médicos que siguen esta línea recetan varios remedios, en tomas separadas a lo largo del día, que cubren en conjunto todos los síntomas del enfermo.

Complejistas: Utilizan fórmulas compuestas de varios remedios, que se toman juntos.

Normas de prescripción y posología

La elección del grado de dilución y ritmo de administración del remedio homeopático, depende mucho del médico que prescribe. Sin embargo, existen unas normas que resumimos esquemáticamente.

Enfermedades agudas

Enfermedades agudas con similitud local: Se utilizan diluciones bajas (hasta la 6 CH), en varias tomas diarias. Cuanto más aguda sea la enfermedad, mayor será la frecuencia de administración del medicamento.

Enfermedades agudas con similitud general: Se emplean diluciones medias (hasta la 15 CH), y la frecuencia de las tomas suele ser de 1 ó 2 veces al día.

Enfermedades agudas con similitud mental: Si aparecen síntomas netos y precisos se usarán diluciones altas (a partir de la 30 CH), en tomas muy espaciadas.

Un ejemplo: «Amigdalitis aguda».

Síntomas mentales Tratamiento: BELLADONA 30 CH	— Delirios y alucinaciones	Síntomas locales	— Comienzo brusco — Garganta muy roja, seca, con dolor y dificultad al tragar.
		Tratamiento: BELLADONA 4 ó 5 CH	— Ganglios del cuello aumentados y dolorosos.
Síntomas generales Tratamiento: BELLADONA 7 ó 9 CH	— Fiebre alta — Sudor que alterna con escalofríos. — Mucha sed.	Estas normas de prescipción están sometidas a la Ley de Semejanzas: LA DILUCION SERA TANTO MAS ELEVADA CUANTO MAYOR SEA LA SEMEJANZA.	

Las tomas del medicamento deberán ser espaciadas, a medida que la enfermedad vaya remitiendo.

Enfermedades crónicas

En general se prescriben diluciones medias o altas, dependiendo de la antigüedad de la enfermedad, y en tomas muy espaciadas. A mayor similitud de síntomas mentales, se utilizan diluciones más altas.

En realidad, la pauta de tratamiento es cuestión de experiencia personal. Lo fundamental es respetar la regla de oro de la Homeopatía: la aplicación de la similitud, cualquiera que sea el método que se use.

Forma de tomar el medicamento homeopático

Debido a las pequeñas dosis que contienen los medicamentos homeopáticos, es necesario seguir una serie de normas para conseguir una mayor eficacia terapéutica.

Los gránulos son, quizá, la forma de presentación más utilizada, y a la que nos referimos en las siguientes páginas correspondientes al tratamiento de algunas enfermedades agudas comunes. En su toma han de observarse las siguientes precauciones:

— No deben ser manipulados; es conveniente pasarlos del bote a su tapa y de ésta, directamente a la boca.

— La mejor vía de administración del remedio es la sublingual, dejando que los gránulos se disuelvan lentamente, sin tragarlos, masticarlos ni beber agua u otros líquidos.

— La toma del medicamento ha de hacerse al menos 10 minutos antes de las comidas o bien 2 horas después.

— Es necesario evitar el tabaco y la utilización de dentífricos mentolados inmediatamente antes o después de la toma del medicamento.

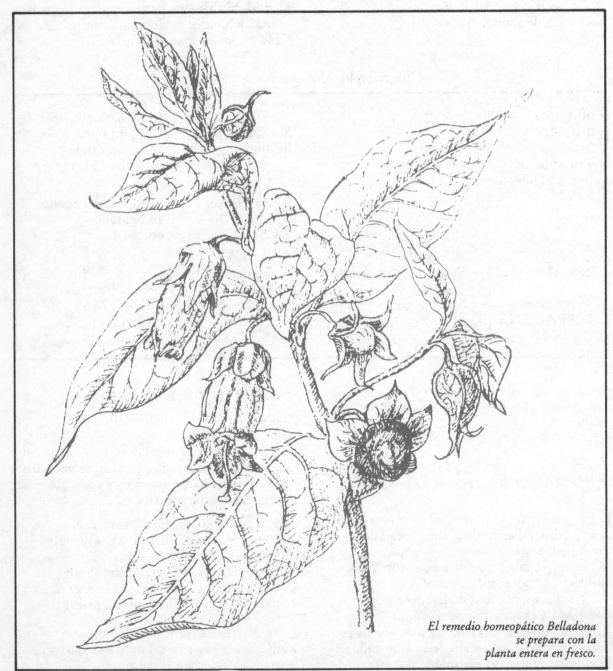

El remedio homeopático Belladona se prepara con la planta entera en fresco.

Tratamiento de algunas enfermedades agudas frecuentes

emos recogido a continuación algunas enfermedades agudas y su tratamiento homeopático, con el fin de orientar acerca de los medicamentos que puedan aliviarlas, aunque sea transitoriamente.

Las situaciones crónicas tienen un tratamiento más complejo que requiere una visión individual y muy completa del sujeto.

En cada epígrafe reseñamos algunos medicamentos de los que se prescriben más a menudo, aunque obviamente no significa que sean éstos los únicos útiles, ni que resuelvan todos los casos.

Personalmente, utilizamos esta medicación en una potencia 5 CH y en una dosis de tres gránulos por toma, pudiendo repetirse ésta entre cada 15 minutos y 3-4 horas, dependiendo de la intensidad de los síntomas y alargando los intervalos, a medida que el cuadro mejora.

Aftas

Son pequeñas lesiones ulcerosas de la mucosa de la boca, localizadas principalmente en lengua, cara interna de mejilla y labios.

Aparecen a cualquier edad, pero son más frecuentes en la infancia y adolescencia.

Son benignas, pero pueden llegar a ser tan dolorosas que dificulten la articulación de las palabras, la masticación y la succión en los lactantes.

Es frecuente su aparición repetitiva en algunas personas.

Baptisia tinctoria

— Ulceraciones de color rojo oscuro, muy dolorosas, en lengua y mucosa bucal.

— Lengua blanca con papilas rojas, hinchada, seca y dolorosa, como las encías.

— Color rojo, sin brillo, de faringe, amígdalas y velo de paladar.

— Gusto amargo y aliento muy fétido.

Borax

— Aftas muy dolorosas en lengua y cara interna de las mejillas, que sangran al menor roce.

— Hay aumento de salivación y calor en la boca, con sequedad y sed.

— Fundamentalmente en niños y lactantes que se encuentran nerviosos, sobresaltados y gritan cuando van a mamar, rehusando el seno.

Mercurius solubilis

— Ulceraciones irregulares, poco profundas, rodeadas de una zona enrojecida y recubiertas de un exudado amarillo.

— Dolores quemantes, fundamentalmente al contacto con alimentos ácidos o salados, que empeoran por la noche.

— Aliento fétido, con salivación exagerada, gusto metálico y lengua amarillenta, que conserva la impresión de los dientes.

— Sed intensa de bebidas frías.

Nitric acidum

— Ulceraciones irregulares, sobre la lengua o cara interna de las mejillas, con fondo rojo o recubiertas de un exudado blanquecino.

— Dolores agudos «como si tuviera clavada una espina».

— Encías hinchadas y sangrantes. Lengua roja o blanco-amarillenta.

— Salivación abundante y aliento fétido.

— Se suelen acompañar de fisuras en los ángulos de la boca.

Sulphuric acidum

— Indicado en las aftas de los lactantes.

— Ulceraciones en placas, sobre la lengua, encías o toda la boca, recubiertas de un exudado blanquecino o amarillento.

— Lengua hinchada.

— Salivación abundante y aliento fétido.

— El niño huele «agrio», a pesar de bañarle.

Amigdalitis aguda

Es la inflamación de las amígdalas, órganos pares situados en la faringe, que cumplen una importante función defensiva.

Estos son algunos de los remedios homeopáticos más usados en su tratamiento:

Apis mellifica

— Garganta hinchada y enrojecida.

— Dolor ardiente y punzante, que se agrava al tragar líquidos calientes y mejora con bebidas, gargarismos y compresas frías.

— Fiebre elevada, con ausencia total de sed.

— Aparición extraordinariamente brusca de toda la sintomatología.

Belladonna

— Garganta, amígdalas y lengua de color rojo brillante, fundamentalmente en el lado derecho.

— Sensación de sequedad y estrechez al tragar.

— Ganglios del cuello aumentados de volumen y dolorosos.

— Fiebre con calor seco o sudores, que alternan con escalofríos, delirio; cara roja, caliente; mirada brillante y taquicardia.

Ferrum phosphoricum

— Garganta inflamada, roja, seca y muy dolorida, sobre todo al tragar. Dolores ardientes.

— Fiebre con piel seca y sudores nocturnos que no mejoran el cuadro. Pulso rápido, lleno y blando.

— Se administra especialmente al comienzo de la angina.

Phytolacca

— Garganta de color rojo oscuro, con amígdalas rojas e hinchadas, con puntos blancos que a veces se unen formando placas. Peor el lado derecho.

— «Siente como una bola de hierro al rojo en la garganta». Los dolores empeoran con bebidas calientes, que prácticamente no puede tragar, y al flexionar la cabeza.

— Ganglios del cuello aumentados de volumen.

— Gran postración, con dolor en músculos y huesos. Puede haber fiebre elevada.

Mercurius solubilis

— Garganta roja o cobriza, con angina principalmente derecha, con tendencia a supurar.

— Dolor agudo al tragar, que se extiende al oído o a los ganglios submaxilares, que están muy sensibles.

— Lengua dentada, aliento muy fétido y salivación abundante con necesidad de tragar constantemente.

— Fiebre con sudores nocturnos, que no mejoran el cuadro.

Cefaleas

El dolor de cabeza es una afección muy frecuente, que puede obedecer a causas muy variadas: trastornos oculares, sinusitis, alteraciones hepáticas, hipertensión arterial, lesiones de la columna vertebral, etc. Sin embargo, lo más frecuente es que sea debido a malos hábitos de vida —mala alimentación, estreñimiento, abuso de café, tabaco y alcohol...—, falta de descanso, preocupaciones excesivas...

Para lograr una mejoría permanente, será necesaria la modificación de los factores causales.

Bryonia

— Cefaleas violentas, de cualquier localización, con la sensación de que la «cabeza fuera a estallar».

— Se presentan por la mañana al despertar o con el primer movimiento.

— Hay náuseas, vómitos y deseo de acostarse y permanecer tranquilo en la oscuridad.

— Se puede encontrar lengua blanca, mucha sed y estreñimiento habitual.

— Mejoran por el reposo y la presión local y se agravan con el movimiento (al toser, al levantarse, al caminar, al mover los ojos o la cabeza...).

Belladonna

— Cefaleas pulsátiles, martilleantes, violentas.

— La cara está roja, congestionada, y la mirada brillante.

— Aparecen o empeoran de las 16 horas a las 3 de la madrugada. Se agravan por el calor de la cama, por movimiento, luz y ruido. Mejoran en una habitación oscura, cerrando los ojos, con la cabeza apoyada, y por frío local.

Gelsemium

— Cefaleas aturdidoras, enloquecedoras, con sensación de estallido, que comienzan en región cervical y occipital y se van extendiendo hacia arriba, por toda la cabeza, hacia frente u ojos.

— Precedidas por trastornos visuales (visión nublada, doble...) que a menudo persisten durante la cefalea. Hay gran pesadez de párpados —no se pueden mantener abiertos los ojos.

— Generalmente, no van acompañadas de naúseas y vómitos, sino de debilidad y temblores, con gran cansancio, aturdimiento y deseo de estar solo.

— Empeoran hacia las 10 de la mañana, y al mover la cabeza, por esfuerzos mentales, emociones, por el calor del sol, por fumar... Mejoran por una micción profusa, acostado con la cabeza alta, presionando, y por calor local.

Iris versicolor

— Jaquecas frontales o hemicráneas, generalmente de origen hepático. En la mitad derecha de la cabeza o frente.

— Precedida o acompañada de visión borrosa; con naúseas y vómitos biliosos intensos. El hígado suele estar agrandado y sensible.

— Aparecen o se agravan después del desayuno, por esfuerzos mentales y por frío.

Nux vomica

— Especialmente frontal y en el lado izquierdo, aunque puede afectar a toda la cabeza.

— Generalmente, debidas a excesos de tabaco, café y alcohol; comilonas o falta de sueño, en sujetos de vida sedentaria.

— Sobre todo por la mañana, al despertar o después de comer.

— A menudo acompañada de sabor de boca amarga, naúseas y vómitos; gran somnolencia diurna e irritabilidad.

Iris versicolor

Sanguinaria

— Jaquecas o hemicráneas muy intensas, que aparecen periódicamente —«cada 7 días»—. Comienzan en región occipital y se fijan, sobre todo, en sien y ojo derecho. Con sensación de latidos y vómitos.

— No tolera la luz, olores ni movimiento. Mejora acostado en la oscuridad, al dormir y presionando la cabeza con las manos.

Conjuntivitis aguda

La conjuntivitis es la inflamación de la conjuntiva, delgada membrana que cubre la parte anterior del globo ocular y la interna de los párpados.

Puede producirse por causas muy diversas: infecciosas, irritativas, alérgicas...

Argentum nitricum

— Conjuntivitis granulosa aguda, con conjuntivas muy rojas, fundamentalmente en los ángulos de los ojos y la carúncula lagrimal (lado interno).

— Hinchazón de párpados, lagrimeo y gran intolerancia a la luz.

— Abundante secreción mucopurulenta o amarillenta, con párpados pegados por la mañana.

— Empeora por el calor y esfuerzos como leer y coser. Mejora por aplicaciones frías.

— Buen remedio para la conjuntivitis del recién nacido.

Belladonna

— Conjuntivitis aguda, provocada por frío, con conjuntivas muy rojas y brillantes.

— Intolerancia a la luz, con sensación de sequedad y calor en los ojos y dilatación pupilar.

— Lagrimeo corrosivo.

— A menudo hay fiebre, cara roja y sensación de pulsaciones en todo el cuerpo.

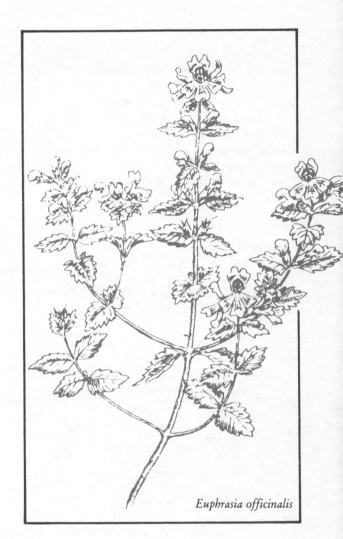

Euphrasia officinalis

Euphrasia

— Conjuntivas rojas con vasos semejantes a una red, desde los ángulos del ojo hacia el centro.

— Párpados muy inflamados e incluso ulcerados en su borde.

— Lagrimeo ardiente e irritante, que empeora con el viento y que casi siempre va acompañado de rinitis, con secreción abundante y no irritante.

— Dolor presivo en el ángulo interno del ojo y sensación de ardor o arenilla, que obliga a pestañear continuamente.

— Intolerancia a la luz, sobre todo a la artificial.

Mercurius solubilis

— Conjuntivitis aguda provocada por frío.

— Conjuntiva enrojecida, así como los párpados que están muy inflamados.

— Secreción abundante, purulenta o amarillenta e irritante.

— Intolerancia a la luz y lagrimeo abundante al aire libre.

— Empeoramiento de todos los síntomas por el calor.

Pulsatilla

— Secreción purulenta, amarilla, espesa, no irritante, acumulada en el ángulo interno del ojo, fundamentalmente por la mañana, al despertar.

— Ardor y picor que empeora al anochecer.

— Lagrimeo e intolerancia a la luz.

— Todos los síntomas mejoran con frío y al aire libre.

Diarrea

Se denomina así a la emisión de heces fluidas, pastosas o líquidas, que suele ir unida al aumento del número de deposiciones. Causadas por múltiples factores, como trangresiones o sobrecargas dietéticas, alimentos en mal estado, uso reiterado de laxantes o enemas, infecciones, nerviosismo...

Junto a cualquier tratamiento es fudamental la dieta, a base de líquidos y alimentos astringentes.

Aloe

— Deseo imperioso, urgente, de evacuar, que lo levanta temprano de la cama, con gran dificultad para contener las heces que, a menudo, salen involuntariamente.

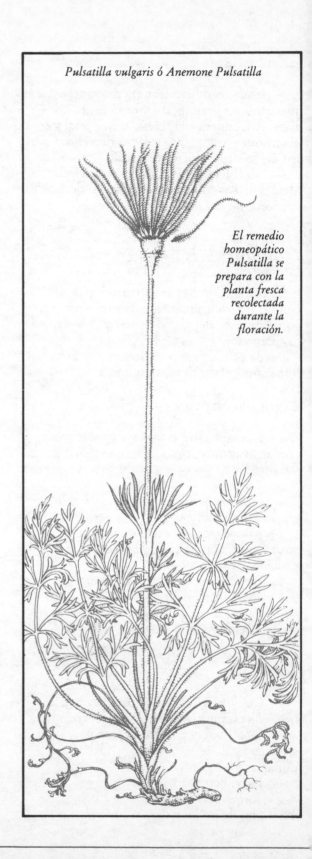

Pulsatilla vulgaris ó Anemone Pulsatilla

El remedio homeopático Pulsatilla se prepara con la planta fresca recolectada durante la floración.

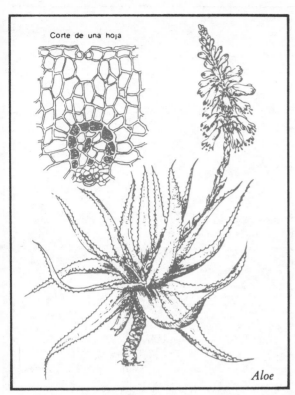

Corte de una hoja

Aloe

— Con diarrea en chorro, muy abundante y fétida, y flatulencia.

— Esta diarrea puede estar provocada por ingestión de fruta y empeora en verano.

Arsenicum album

— Diarrea, sobre todo después de medianoche, a menudo con vómitos.

— Las deposiciones son oscuras, de olor pútrido, no muy abundantes y excoriantes, con dolores ardientes, como «fuego en el recto», mientras defeca y después. Están seguidas de gran postración.

— Suelen estar provocadas por bebidas o comidas frías. Empeoran de noche y por frío.

China

— Diarrea después de mediodía y por la noche; después de comer fruta; en tiempo caluroso. Otras veces la diarrea es periódica.

— Heces evacuadas sin dolor que, aunque blandas, salen con gran dificultad. Con gran flatulencia de todo el abdomen, que mejora por la presión.

— Boca seca, con sabor amargo. Gran debilidad.

Mercurius solubilis

— Diarrea a menudo nocturna, sobre todo por enfriamiento.

— Las deposiciones son acuosas y excoriantes, con sensación de no terminar de evacuar.

— Aliento fétido, secreción salivar abundante y sudores nocturnos profusos.

Podophyllum

— Diarrea por la mañana temprano o antes del mediodía.

— Heces muy abundantes y fétidas, amarillentas, en chorro, sin dolor y seguidas de sensación de evacuación incompleta y gran debilidad.

Veratrum album

— Diarrea extremadamente abundante, acuosa, precedida de muchos dolores y calambres. Puede haber vómitos intensos y continuos.

— Las heces son evacuadas con gran deseo y expulsadas con fuerza. La diarrea está seguida de gran postración, sensación de vacío y debilidad en el vientre.

— Suele haber sudoración abundante y fría, sobre todo de la frente.

Dismenorrea (Menstruación dolorosa)

— Aunque la menstruación dolorosa puede estar producida por alteraciones orgánicas, aquí nos referimos a las puramente funcionales, no justificadas por lesión alguna y que constituyen la mayoría de las dismenorreas.

Belladonna

— Reglas adelantadas, muy abundantes, con sangre color rojo vivo, mezclada con coágulos.

— Dolores violentos, con sensación de presión en parte baja del abdomen. Estos dolores aparecen y desaparecen bruscamente.

— Mejoran estando sentada y se agravan por el movimiento y al caminar.

Chamomilla

— Reglas adelantadas, muy abundantes, de sangre negra con coágulos.

— Dolores antes y durante la menstruación, muy intensos, en accesos. De tipo calambroide, opresivos o de tironeo, o como dolores de parto.

— No puede descansar tranquila, está constantemente agitada, inquieta, impaciente y de humor insoportable. No tolera nada ni a nadie.

Magnesia phosphorica

— Reglas adelantadas, con sangre negra en filamentos.

— Dolores como calambres o como de parto, de predominio derecho, antes o durante la menstruación (tienden a desaparecer al comenzar ésta).

— Mejoran mucho por calor, presión local y doblándose en dos.

Pulsatilla

— Reglas de sangre oscura, atrasadas, escasas y de corta duración.

— Dolores antes y durante la

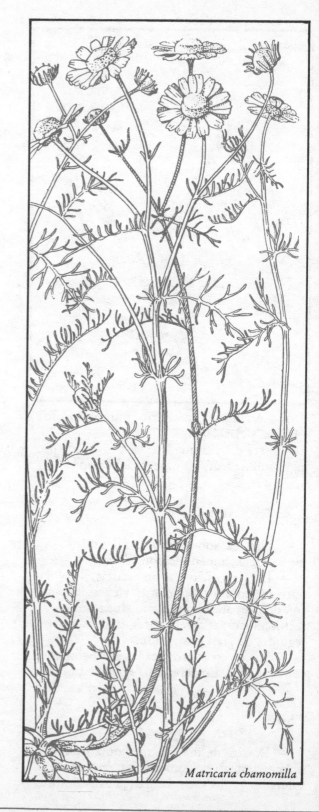

Matricaria chamomilla

menstruación, que la hacen llorar. En crisis, como de tironeo hacia abajo, calambres o semejantes a un parto. Puede haber diarrea durante y después de la regla.

— Empeoran estando acostada y mejoran al aire libre y por el frío local.
— Mentalidad característica: llanto suave, con deseo de consuelo, afecto y compañía.

Viburnum opulus

— Reglas retardadas y cortas.
— Dolores, especialmente premenstruales, que van disminuyendo a medida que se instala el flujo menstrual.
— En crisis, como de tironeo hacia abajo, calambres o parecidos a un parto.

— Dolor en la región sacra, que irradia a los muslos. Calambres abdominales bruscos, con dolores alrededor del ombligo.

Dispepsia (Dificultad para la digestión)

La mayoría de las veces está provocada y mantenida por inobservancia de ciertas reglas de higiene alimentaria: alimentación incorrecta (grasas, picantes, alcohol, bebidas gaseosas...), mala masticación, prisa, fatiga o nerviosismo, etc.

El tratamiento puede aliviar las molestias, pero el enfermo no se curará si no modifica sus malos hábitos alimentarios.

Los síntomas pueden ser muy variados, como veremos a continuación.

Antimonium crudum

— Indicado en trastornos digestivos causados por ingestión de alimentos de difícil digestión o en cantidad exagerada.
— La lengua está cubierta por una capa espesa y blanca.
— Hay eructos con sabor y olor de la comida, náuseas (sólo por pensar u oler alimentos) y vómitos agotadores.
— Sensación de plenitud y aversión a la comida.

China

— Indigestión sobre todo por frutas; por tomar mucho té, leche o alimentos ácidos o crudos.
— Sensación de plenitud y pesadez después de comer, aunque haya comido poco. Se sacia fácilmente.
— Eructos ácidos o amargos. Regurgitaciones. Gran flatulencia dolorosa, con estómago muy sensible al menor contacto.

— Diarrea indolora, con restos de alimentos sin digerir, que va acompañada de mucha flatulencia y empeora después de comer.

Lycopodium

— Indigestión por alimentos fríos, flatulentos, repollo, cebolla, ostras...

— Mucha hambre, pero se sacia rápidamente, apenas empieza a comer. Con gran sensación de plenitud después de haber comido, aunque sea un solo bocado, si son alimentos que le sientan mal.

— Hay eructos ardientes y sensación de ardor en la faringe. A veces náuseas y vómitos. Gran flatulencia y distensión en la región inferior del abdomen, que mejora expulsando gases.

— Mejora por la mañana y empeora entre las 14 y 20 horas.

Nux vomica

— Indigestión sobre todo por abundante toma de alcohol o café, por comidas frías, leche, ácidos, grasas, farináceas... y por exceso de actividad mental.

— Hay sensación de pesadez sorda en región gástrica, pero no inmediatamente después de comer, sino una hora más tarde. Con ardor, eructos ácidos y regurgitaciones. Náuseas y vómitos que lo alivian.

— Lengua limpia delante y blanco-amarillenta detrás, con mal sabor. Estreñimiento, con deseos urgentes e ineficaces de evacuar.

— Puede haber cefaleas y somnolencia después de comer. Irritabilidad e impaciencia.

Es el mejor remedio para los efectos de excesos alimentarios o bebidas alcohólicas.

Pulsatilla

— Indigestión por alimentos grasos y masas.

— Boca seca, sin sed y con gusto amargo por la mañana. Lengua blanca o amarillenta.

— Ligero dolor y sensación de distensión gástrica después de las comidas, con necesidad de aflojarse la ropa.

— Digestión lenta, con molesta sensación de hambre y eructos con sabor de alimentos.

— Náuseas después de las comidas y vómitos escasos.

Estreñimiento

En la gran mayoría de los casos, se produce por dos motivos principales: por ingestión de alimentos que no dejan residuos, como ocurre con tanta frecuencia hoy en día, o por mal hábito en la defecación, al resistirse a ella por falta de tiempo u oportunidad. La utilización de laxantes acentúa progresivamente la falta de tono intestinal.

Aunque el estreñimiento suele ser un estado crónico, en este apartado nos referimos a las manifestaciones agudas, que se pueden producir ocasionalmente en personas con tránsito intestinal normal.

Clásicamente encontramos tres tipos de enfermos:

— Algunos no pueden defecar nunca naturalmente; no tienen ningún deseo (ALUMINA, BRYONIA, OPIUM).

— Otros tienen dificultad para expulsar las heces, tienen deseos, pero insuficientes (NUX VOMICA, PLUMBUM, SULPHUR).

— Hay otro grupo de enfermos con deseos que no pueden ser satisfechos, las heces no pueden ser expulsadas (LYCOPODIUM, SILICEA).

Alumina

— El sujeto hace grandes esfuerzos para evacuar sus heces, que son escasas, como bolitas duras, oscuras o adherentes como la arcilla.

— Inactividad rectal: «no hay deseos ni posibilidad de defecar, hasta que hay una gran acumulación de heces».

Bryonia

— Estreñimiento sin deseos, provocado por extrema sequedad de la mucosa intestinal.
— Las heces son muy grandes, secas, duras, como «quemadas», y sólo son evacuadas después de grandes esfuerzos.

Opium

— No hay ningún dolor ni deseo de defecar. Total inactividad rectal.
— Las heces tienen forma de pequeñas bolitas, secas, duras, de color oscuro.
— Es un estreñimiento propio del embarazo, de ancianos, de personas con hábitos sedentarios; en los viajes; por abuso de drogas.

Nux vomica

— Hay mal funcionamiento de los movimientos peristálticos del intestinto, con deseos constantes pero ineficaces para defecar. «No tiene jamás la sensación de tener vacío el recto».
— El vientre está distendido y las heces son duras, secas y se expulsan en pequeña cantidad y con gran dificultad.
— Por abuso de laxantes, en viejos, hábitos sedentarios, en los viajes, durante el embarazo y menstruación.

Plumbum

— Heces negras, secas y duras como las de Opium, pero mientras el enfermo de Opium no experimenta deseos de defecar, el de Plumbum tiene deseos urgentes, que no puede satisfacer más que de forma insuficiente.
— Sufre una «contracción anal», con dolor que remonta el ano de abajo hacia arriba.

Sulphur

— Deseos urgentes, a veces violentos, que no pueden ser satisfechos.
— Heces expulsadas con grandes esfuerzos y sensación de «calor en el recto».
— Alternancia de estreñimiento y diarrea.

Lycopodium

— Deseos ineficaces por contracción del recto, que impide la salida de las heces, provocando dolor durante la defecación.
— La deposición puede ser de heces duras primero, y blandas después, o bien elimina heces mezcladas con materia líquida.
— Puede acompañarse de gran flatulencia y hemorroides.

Silicea

— Las heces son duras y el estreñimiento tiene esta característica: hay necesidad marcada de evacuar, pero cuando la deposición sale un poco del recto, vuelve a entrar, como si éste no tuviera fuerza suficiente.

Cuando el estreñimiento no tiene caracteres bien definidos, puede recurrirse a la alternancia de NUX VOMICA y SULPHUR.

Fiebre

En el estado de salud, la temperatura del cuerpo se mantiene dentro de unos límites estrechos. Existen pequeñas diferencias individuales e incluso hay una variación normal en la temperatura a lo largo del día, ya que sube a medida que éste avanza, alcanzando un máximo entre las 18-22 horas y descendiendo después lentamente hasta llegar a su mínimo entre las 2-4 horas.

La elevación de la temperatura sobre las cifras normales o fiebre, es un acompañante habitual de enfermedades muy diversas.

Aconitum napellus

— Fiebre que aparece por exposición al frío seco.

— Temperatura alta con piel roja y ardiente. La cara, que también está roja, empalidece bruscamente al erguirse en la cama.

— Escalofríos, desde las extremidades, al pecho y cabeza, que empeoran con el movimiento.

— No hay sudor. Cuando éste comienza ya no está indicado Aconitum.

— Sed inextinguible de grandes cantidades de agua fría.

— Ansiedad, inquietud y miedo.

— Empeoramiento nocturno.

— Pulso lleno y fuerte.

— Util en trastornos inflamatorios agudos febriles de comienzo brusco, antes de que aparezca una localización.

Apis mellifica

— Fiebre con ausencia de sed, que empeora por el calor (hay tendencia a destaparse).

— Escalofríos por la tarde (principalmente de 3 a 5).

— Puede haber sudores mínimos, alternantes con períodos de piel caliente y seca.

— Sensibilidad al menor tacto.

Belladonna

— Fiebre elevada que puede acompañarse de delirio y alucinaciones, fundamentalmente visuales.

— Piel caliente, roja y que irradia calor. La cara está pálida cuando el enfermo se acuesta y roja cuando se incorpora.

— La fiebre comienza con escalofríos en los brazos.

— Calor seco o con sudores, que se producen principalmente en la cabeza.

— Mejora por el calor, por lo que tiene aversión a destaparse.

— Labios, boca, lengua y garganta secos y ardorosos.

— Agravación de los síntomas por la noche.

— Buen remedio para cuadros de aparición brusca, con las características anteriores y sensación de latidos o pulsaciones en todo el cuerpo.

Bryonia alba

— Fiebre media que empeora al anochecer.

— Escalofríos que comienzan en la punta de los dedos, principalmente por la mañana y por la noche, con sudores de olor ácido que alivian los síntomas.

— Sed intensa de bebidas frías, de grandes cantidades y a largos intervalos.

— Boca, lengua y garganta muy secas.

— Violento dolor de cabeza, con sensación de que le fuera a estallar.

— Sensibilidad aumentada en todo el cuerpo y fatiga.

— Mejora con el reposo, por lo que el enfermo descansa completamente inmóvil en su cama.

— Pulso rápido.

Ferrum phosphoricum

— Fiebre no muy elevada, con escalofríos de poca intensidad.

— Piel caliente y seca, con sudores copiosos nocturnos que no alivian.

— Pulso lleno, blando y rápido.

— Es un remedio muy útil en el comienzo de los procesos agudos.

Gripe

Es una enfermedad infecciosa aguda, de origen vírico. Suele ser benigna, pero en ocasiones puede tener más gravedad, dependiendo del carácter de la epidemia (recordemos la de 1918-19, con más de 20 millones de muertos), de la edad (más severa en ancianos), y del estado previo del individuo (más grave cuando existe alguna alteración precedente, como patología cardíaca, renal...).

Bryonia alba

— Escalofríos que comienzan en las puntas de los dedos y los labios, con fiebre, fundamentalmente por la noche, y sudor que mejora los síntomas.
— Dolor de espalda y extremidades, que empeora por el más mínimo movimiento y mejora en reposo y con la presión fuerte. Fatiga.
— Intenso dolor de cabeza (como si le fuera a estallar) y de los ojos.
— Boca seca, así como labios y lengua, que está cubierta de una capa blanquecina.
— Mucha sed de grandes cantidades de agua fría cada vez.

Eupatorium perfoliatum

— Comienzo con intensos escalofríos y temblores, más intensos de 7 a 9 de la mañana.
— Fiebre con sed, que desaparece cuando suda.
— Sensación de magullamiento general, con intensos dolores óseos y musculares, principalmente en región lumbar y pantorrillas.
— Fuerte dolor de cabeza, con aumento de sensibilidad de cuero cabelludo y ojos.

— Náuseas y vómitos biliosos o alimenticios.
— Enfermo muy agitado; no puede estar quieto, aunque el movimiento no le alivia.

Gelsemium

— Fiebre intensa con calor en cara y cabeza y manos y pies fríos.
— Escalofríos intensos, que comienzan en manos y pies y recorren la espalda de arriba hacia abajo.
— Ausencia de sed.
— Dolores musculares, con gran sensación de pesadez y cansancio. Abatimiento general y debilidad. Temblores.
— Dolor de cabeza, «como si una venda le apretara por encima de los ojos», con párpados pesados.
— Cara color rojo oscuro, con expresión aturdida.
— Coriza agudo con estornudos y secreción acuosa irritante. Garganta roja, seca y ardiente.

Rhus toxicodendron

— Gripe con fiebre y escalofríos, que producen la sensación de salpicaduras con agua helada. Empeoramiento por la noche.
— Sed, con deseos de agua o leche fría, durante la fiebre y no cuando hay escalofríos.
— Dolores de espalda y miembros, que empeoran al comenzar a moverse y mejoran prosiguiendo el movimiento.
— Cansancio y dolor de cabeza, que se alivia cuando se produce hemorragia nasal.
— Lengua seca, con un triángulo rojo en la punta.
— Gran inquietud, que le hace dar vueltas en la cama.
— Gripe que se produce después de haberse expuesto a humedad o lluvia.

Hemorroides

Son dilataciones de las venas hemorroidales, que se hallan en el ano y última porción del recto. El estreñimiento, embarazo y abuso de comidas irritantes, bebidas alcohólicas y laxantes, son factores que influyen en su producción y persistencia.

En su tratamiento, es fundamental corregir el estreñimiento y los hábitos dietéticos, así como los trastornos hepáticos, si los hubiera.

Aesculus

— Hemorroides de color púrpura, rara vez sangrantes.

— Sensación de plenitud, ardor, sequedad y pinchazos, como si el recto estuviera lleno de espinas.

— Estreñimiento habitual con heces duras y secas, de evacuación costosa, que se suele acompañar de dolor sacro-lumbar pulsátil y se sigue de dolor ardiente en el ano durante varias horas.

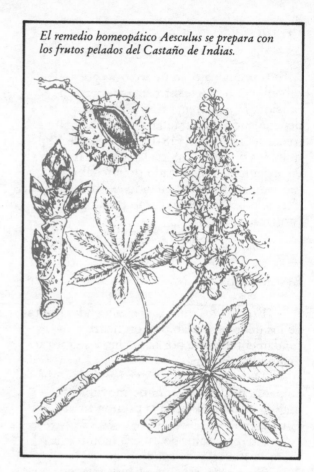

El remedio homeopático Aesculus se prepara con los frutos pelados del Castaño de Indias.

Muriatic acidum

— Hemorroides hinchadas y azules, extremadamente sensibles que no toleran el más mínimo contacto.

— Dolores ardientes, que empeoran al defecar y estando sentado.

— Sangran periódicamente.

— Mejoran con el calor y se agravan con las aplicaciones frías.

Nux vomica

— Hemorroides internas, con picor y dolor que aumenta por la noche.

— Dolores cortantes después de la defecación, que también suele producir hemorragias.

— Se alivian mediante frío local.

— Suele haber estreñimiento, con deseos urgentes e ineficaces de evacuar.

— Tratamiento muy útil en personas de vida sedentaria y que han abusado de estimulantes (alcohol, tabaco, condimentos...).

Hamamelis

— Hemorroides azuladas que sangran abundantemente al defecar. Hemorragias de sangre oscura, seguidas de postración desproporcionada con la pérdida.

— Muy dolorosas, con pulsaciones en recto y ardores en ano y sensación de plenitud en la región sacro-lumbar.

— Se alivian con baños de asiento fríos.

Aloe

— Hemorroides grandes, azuladas, prominentes, «como racimos de uvas».

— Dolores ardientes que mejoran con agua fría y no toleran el menor contacto.

— Sangran fácilmente.

— Intenso picor y ardor anal por la noche, que le impiden dormir.

— Tendencia a la diarrea inmediatamente después de haber comido.

— Gran cantidad de gases y dificultad para retener las heces, que tienden a salir involuntariamente.

Hamamelis virginiana

Parotiditis (Paperas)

Es la inflamación de las glándulas parótidas. Su causa es vírica y afecta generalmente a niños en edad escolar y adolescentes.

Suele tener un curso benigno, aunque, a veces, puede dar lugar a complicaciones (inflamación de testículos, ovarios, páncreas, meninges...), principalmente cuando se produce en adultos.

Belladonna

— Es un remedio muy importante, especialmente al principio de la inflamación y cuando ésta comienza en la parótida derecha.

— Hinchazón brusca de las glándulas, que están calientes y con intensa sensibilidad al tacto.

— Dolores lancinantes, agudos, que irradian al oído y empeoran al masticar y por otros movimientos.

— Boca seca, caliente, y lengua con papilas enrojecidas. Sed intensa.

— Fiebre alta con cara roja y dilatación pupilar.

— Comienzo brusco de todos los síntomas.

Mercurius solubilis

— Inflamación de las parótidas, fundamentalmente la derecha, y de las glándulas sublinguales y submaxilares.

— Dificultad para abrir la boca y dolor al tragar.

— Lengua blanda, cubierta de una capa amarillenta y con las marcas de los dientes sobre ella.

— Aliento fétido y salivación abundante, principalmente de noche y durmiendo (moja la almohada).

— Fiebre moderada con escalofríos y sudores que aumentan por la noche y no mejoran los síntomas.

Pulsatilla

— Es el medicamento más importante para el tratamiento de la orquitis (inflamación de testículos), que se puede dar en algunos casos como complicación de la parotiditis.

— Ausencia de sed con boca seca y mal gusto, principalmente por la mañana, al despertar.

— Fiebre con escalofríos. Manos y pies ardientes que buscan sitios fríos, con tendencia a destaparse.

— El enfermo se encuentra muy sensible, mimoso y llorón y está mejor al aire libre.

Rhus toxicodendron

— Inflamación parotídea, principalmente la izquierda.

— La piel sobre la glándula está de color rojo.

— Puede haber también afectación de las glándulas submaxilares que están hinchadas y duras.

— Sensación de pinchazos al tragar.

— Estado general muy alterado, con fiebre elevada y dolores en los miembros y región lumbar, que mejoran por el movimiento.

— El paciente está muy agitado, fundamentalmente por la noche.

Picaduras de insectos

Apis mellifica

— Dolores punzantes y quemantes, como producidos por agujas enrojecidas al fuego.

— Gran sensibilidad al menor contacto.

— Empeora por el calor y se alivia con el frío local.

— Enorme hinchazón alrededor de la picadura, de color rosado pálido.

Culex musca

— Indicado en picaduras de mosquitos.

— Gran picor y ardor local.

— Mejora durante el rascado pero empeora después.

Ledum palustre

— Es el principal remedio en las picaduras de insectos, fundamentalmente de abejas y mosquitos.

— Dolores punzantes o pulsátiles, que empeoran por el calor y mejoran por el frío local, a pesar de que la zona afectada suele estar fría al tacto, pálida y dormida.

— Intenso picor.

Urtica urens

— Hinchazón con picor y ardor intolerables, como los producidos por ortigas.

— Empeoramiento por el lavado.

Ortiga menor

Resfriado común

Está producido por diversos virus, al encontrarse el organismo en un estado de menor resistencia, generalmente ocasionado por frío excesivo o por paso de un ambiente caldeado a otro frío, que favorece que los gérmenes exalten su virulencia, provocando la afección, cuyos síntomas son rinitis, faringitis y malestar general.

Allium cepa

— Secreción nasal copiosa, acuosa, que gotea de la nariz excoriando sus bordes y el labio superior. Peor en el lado izquierdo.
— Ojos rojos con intolerancia a la luz y lagrimeo no irritante.
— Constantes estornudos que empeoran al anochecer y en habitación calurosa, mejorando al aire libre.
— El coriza puede extenderse a la garganta y laringe, con sensación de picazón y tos espasmódica.
— Todos los síntomas empeoran al anochecer y en habitación calurosa, mejorando al aire libre.

Kali iodatum

— Congestión de nariz con secreción constante de un líquido acuoso e irritante, que provoca sensación de ardor en las fosas nasales.
— Violentos estornudos y dolor de cabeza por congestión de los senos frontales. Puede haber dolor de garganta.
— Los síntomas mejoran en ambiente cerrado y empeoran al aire libre.

Arsenicum album

— Secreción nasal acuosa, excoriante-ardiente, que irrita el labio superior. Peor en el lado derecho.

— Hay estornudos frecuentes y escalofríos.
— Generalmente producido por frío y corrientes de aire, o por un enfriamiento estando acalorado.
— Se acompaña de sed, ansiedad e inquietud.
— Mejora por calor y bebidas calientes.

Mercurius solubilis

— Obstrucción nasal con secreción acuosa o amarillo-verdosa, a veces con excoriaciones en la mucosa nasal.
— Con laringitis, dolores de garganta o tos.
— Aliento fétido y salivación abundante con sabor metálico.
— Puede haber fiebre, con abundantes sudores nocturnos.
— Empeora por la noche, por frío y en habitación caliente, mejorando a una temperatura media.

Natrum muriaticum

— Secreción «como clara de huevo», con violentos estornudos. Pérdida de gusto y olfato y sensibilidad dolorosa de la nariz que, al cabo de dos o tres días, es reemplazada por sensación de obstrucción de fosas nasales, con respiración difícil.
— Tos violenta, con dolor de cabeza.
— Extrema sensibilidad al frío.

Nux vomica

— Sensación de obstrucción nasal, de pesadez en la región frontal. Por la mañana y por la tarde puede tener secreción acuosa, pero cuando llega la noche, la sequedad se hace muy marcada. Se agrava en habitaciones calientes y mejora al aire libre.
— Hay violentos estornudos y escalofríos, que empeoran al destaparse.

— Cefalea frontal y garganta dolorosa, sensible a la inhalación de aire frío.

— Tos seca, dolorosa, con sensación de estallido de la cabeza, que empeora de noche y por la mañana y mejora por reposo, calor y bebidas calientes.

Pulsatilla

— Alternancia de períodos de sequedad con secreción espesa, amarillo-verdosa, no irritante, que mejora al aire libre.

— Intensos estornudos y pérdida de gusto y olfato.

— Hay ausencia absoluta de sed.

— Todos los síntomas empeoran al anochecer y en ambientes cerrados.

Reumatismo agudo

Bajo el término de «reumatismos» se agrupan una serie de enfermedades con orígenes muy diversos: infecciosos, degenerativos, metabólicos..., y cuya característica común es la afectación de las articulaciones. Sus síntomas más destacados son dolor y rigidez, con o sin inflamación.

A continuación, referimos algunos de los remedios útiles para el tratamiento de la crisis dolorosa aguda.

Aconitum napellus

— Articulaciones hinchadas con fuertes dolores, acompañados de sensación de hormigueo y adormecimiento.

— Las zonas afectadas tienen color rojo brillante y una gran sensibilidad al tacto.

— El enfermo está muy agitado y ansioso.

— Hay empeoramiento nocturno.

— Aparición brusca, por exposición al frío seco.

— Debe utilizarse lo más pronto posible, después de la aparición de los primeros síntomas.

Apis mellifica

— Articulaciones hinchadas, brillantes, tirantes, rosadas y muy sensibles al menor contacto.

— Dolores agudos, punzantes y quemantes (como agujas al rojo vivo), que empeoran por el calor y mejoran por aplicaciones frías.

— Los dolores van de un lado a otro, cambiando bruscamente su localización.

— Aparición muy brusca y violenta de todo el cuadro.

Bryonia alba

— Articulaciones hinchadas, rojas, calientes, con dolores punzantes que empeoran por el movimiento y el tacto; les es imposible realizar el menor movimiento.

— Existe dolor y rigidez muscular.

— El reposo y la presión local, acostándose sobre el lado dolorido, producen alivio.

— Los síntomas se agravan por la noche.

— Los dolores no cambian su localización, como en el caso anterior.

Rhus toxicodendron

— Dolores desgarrantes con sensación de rigidez de tendones, ligamentos y articulaciones.

— Hay un aumento del dolor cuando el paciente comienza a moverse, pero se produce una mejoría evidente si continúa haciéndolo. Sin embargo, el reposo empeora los síntomas.

— El calor alivia el dolor, y el frío y la humedad hacen que éste aparezca o se agrave.

— No puede acostarse sobre el lado doloroso, al revés que Bryonia.

Sarampión

Enfermedad de origen vírico, propia de la infancia, contagiosa, que se caracteriza por presentar una erupción en la piel, fiebre y manifestaciones oculares y respiratorias.

La sintomatología, en un primer período, está constituida por fiebre de intensidad variable y catarro de mucosas, que se asemeja a un estado gripal. Estos son algunos de los remedios que podemos utilizar, junto con los recogidos en el capítulo correspondiente a «Fiebre» y «Tos»:

Belladonna

— Fiebre con piel húmeda y caliente, e incluso con delirio.
— Completamente abatido, con la cara congestionada y las pupilas dilatadas; no soporta la luz.
— Dolor intenso de faringe. Tos seca.

Ferrum phosphoricum

— Fiebre sin agitación ni ansiedad. Piel seca de día, con sudores nocturnos.
— Sensación de «arenilla» dentro de los ojos.
— Cara roja y estornudos frecuentes.

Si hay síntomas en la mucosa bucal:

Mercurius vivus

— Hipersalivación. Saliva espesa y sanguinolenta. Hay sed.
— Encías inflamadas. Lengua saburral. Aliento fétido.

Después de un período de 4-8 días, comienza la erupción, detrás de las orejas y en cara y cuello, desde donde se extiende al tronco y miembros. Suele haber fiebre muy alta. En esta fase podemos utilizar:

Apis mellifica

— Fiebre con calor intenso y deseos de destaparse. Ausencia absoluta de sed.
— Erupción que pincha y arde como picaduras de abeja.
— Conjuntivas rojas con lagrimeo ardiente y fotofobia.
— Faringe roja brillante. Dolor de oídos.

Bryonia

— Fiebre por la noche (peor a las 21 horas), con ausencia de sudoración y sed extrema de grandes cantidades de líquidos fríos. Escalofríos.
— Piel ardiente y seca, con picor intenso.
— Ojos enrojecidos, con fotofobia. Secreción nasal. Cefaleas. Fuerte traqueobronquitis, con punzadas en el tórax al toser.

Gelsemium

— Coloración pálida de la piel, sin manchas acentuadas. Muy congestionado y con los párpados caídos.
— Abatido, postrado, no responde al hablarle.
— Debilidad y temblores en los miembros.
— Secreción nasal acuosa, irritante. Cefalea, sobre todo occipital. Tos desgarrante, con dolores en el pecho.

Rhus toxicodendron

— Fiebre con gran inquietud, especialmente por la noche, que le hace dar vueltas en la cama continuamente o levantarse. Hay sed y la lengua está blanca, con un triángulo rojo en la punta.
— Erupción pruriginosa que empeora por el rascado.

Sulphur

— Fiebre, con la cabeza caliente y los pies fríos. Sed sin apetito.
— Piel seca, áspera, con erupción pruriginosa que empeora por el calor de la cama. Orificios naturales muy rojos.
— Ojos congestionados, con lagrimeo ardiente. Secreción nasal con estornudos. Tos, seca de noche y con expectoración de día.

Tos

Es un mecanismo de gran importancia para mantener permeables las vías aéreas. Su objeto es expulsar de ellas las secreciones o cuerpos extraños. Cuando la tos consigue este fin, se la califica de productiva o eficaz; por el contrario, si no se acompaña de expectoración, se habla de tos seca, improductiva o ineficaz.

La tos productiva ha de repetirse, ya que es un mecanismo de defensa, pero cuando es improductiva o agotadora para el enfermo es conveniente reducirla.

Belladonna

— Tos seca, ronca, persistente, violenta, en crisis, que empeora por la noche.

— Respiración dificultosa que puede provocar o agravar la tos, con la inspiración profunda.

— Sensación de humo o cuerpo extraño en la laringe, con irritación o cosquilleo.

— Gran sequedad de tráquea y laringe.

— Puntos dolorosos en el pecho al toser.

— Afonía.

Drosera

— Tos seca, desgarrante, ronca, agotadora, que se produce en ataques violentos y tan repetidos que pueden provocar sofocación.

— Dolor, al toser, en tórax, con frecuencia debajo de las costillas, que mejora por la presión (el paciente se lleva la mano al punto doloroso) y por el movimiento.

— Cara violácea durante el acceso, así como hemorragias nasales y náuseas y vómitos de mucosidades y alimentos.

— Cosquilleo, sensación de cuerpo extraño y sequedad en laringe. Ronquera.

— La tos empeora con el calor, al acostarse y por la noche. Hay una mejoría general por el movimiento.

Phosphorus

— Tos seca que sacude todo el cuerpo, agotadora, violenta.

— Aparece o empeora acostado en cama (debe sentarse), y más del lado izquierdo (mejora si se da la vuelta hacia el derecho). También agravan la tos, los cambios de temperatura, el frío, los esfuerzos (leer, reír, hablar...).

— Sensación de cuerpo extraño en laringe y de constricción en tórax, «como si tuviera un vendaje apretado alrededor».

— Violento dolor de pecho con la tos (se agarra el tórax con ambas manos).

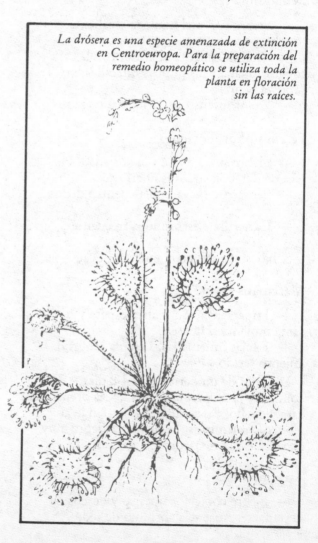

La drósera es una especie amenazada de extinción en Centroeuropa. Para la preparación del remedio homeopático se utiliza toda la planta en floración sin las raíces.

Esta planta es originaria de las selvas húmedas de Brasil

Ipecacuana

— Tos seca, espasmódica, violenta, sofocante, que se produce en cada inspiración.

— Gran cantidad de mucosidades espesas que obstruyen bronquios y alveolos, dificultando la respiración, y que son muy costosas de expulsar.

— Náuseas persistentes con vómitos. Lengua limpia.

— Los síntomas empeoran por el menor movimiento y mejoran tras la expectoración y en reposo.

El remedio homeopático Rumex se prepara a partir del rizoma fresco.

Rumex

— Tos violenta, seca, que empeora al hablar, inspirar, por la presión; fundamentalmente de noche al respirar aire frío, o bien al pasar de un ambiente cálido a otro frío.

— Ardor y escozor en laringe y tráquea.

— Sensación de «magulladura», detrás de las clavículas, y cosquilleo en la garganta, que provoca tos.

— Existe mejoría por el calor.

Traumatismos

Nos referimos en este apartado a las contusiones, lesiones producidas por el choque de un objeto duro contra una parte del cuerpo.

Arnica

— Es el principal medicamento de traumatismos, especialmente de partes blandas (masas musculares), sobre todo cuando hay hematomas.

— El cuerpo o los miembros duelen como si hubiesen sido golpeados. La cama sobre la que está acostado le parece dura, por muy blanda que sea, lo que le hace cambiar a menudo de posición, buscando un lugar más cómodo.

— Arnica acelera la reabsorción del hematoma, calma los dolores y previene la supuración.

Para preparar el remedio homeopático Hypericum se requiere toda la planta en floración

El remedio homeopático Arnica se obtiene a partir de las flores secas.

Hypericum

— Es el medicamento por excelencia de los traumatismos de zonas ricas en terminaciones nerviosas, como los dedos, uñas, plantas de los pies o palmas de las manos.

— En trastornos inmediatos por caída sobre el coxis, con región muy sensible al tacto.

— Hay dolores punzantes intolerables. No soportan que le toquen.

Ledum

— Actúa selectivamente sobre la red capilar sanguínea, sobre todo en regiones con tejidos poco abundantes. En traumatismos del ojo, por un puñetazo, Ledum es inigualable.

— La zona traumatizada se pone fría al tacto.

— Empeora de noche y por calor y movimiento. Mejora por frío y reposo.

— Se puede administrar uno o dos días después de Arnica, para acelerar aún más la reabsorción del hematoma.

Ruta

— Es útil cuando hay traumatismos en el periostio (membrana que cubre los huesos) y tejidos periarticulares, de regiones donde no hay protección de partes blandas (codo, tibia, rodilla, tobillo...). También en músculos y tendones, por esfuerzos desacostumbrados.

— Hay sensación de magulladura y aumento del dolor al apoyar la zona dañada en la cama.

Rhus toxicodendron

— Muy útil después de esfuerzos violentos, ejercicio muscular prolongado y desacostumbrado y torceduras.

— Hay dolores que se agravan en reposo y al comenzar a mover la parte afectada, y van mejorando a medida que el movimiento prosigue.

Urticaria

Afección cutánea caracterizada por la erupción súbita de placas rojizas, de forma y dimensiones variables, acompañadas de intenso picor. Se da en sujetos con una base alérgica y es desencadenada por la ingestión de determinados alimentos (huevos, marisco, chocolate...), picaduras de insectos, factores psíquicos, etc.

Antimonium crudum

— Erupción vesiculosa, roja y dolorosa.

— Ocasionada por alteraciones gástricas; se acompaña de lengua con espesa capa blanquecina.

— Náuseas y vómitos.

— Sensación de «estómago sobrecargado», con eructos frecuentes.

Apis mellifica

— Hinchazón localizada o generalizada de la piel, que aparece bruscamente.

— Enrojecimiento y dolor punzante y quemante, que empeora con el calor y mejora mediante aplicaciones frías.

— Fiebre con ausencia de sed.

Arsenicum album

— Piel muy seca y ardorosa, que empeora por el frío y el rascado, y mejora con el calor.

— Mucho picor. El enfermo se rasca hasta que su piel arde; cuando el escozor se disipa, el picor reaparece.

— Urticaria que aparece después de una intoxicación alimenticia.

Dulcamara

— Urticaria que aparece en personas de piel fina y delicada, provocada o agravada por el frío húmedo.

— Erupción en placas con escamillas.

— Picor que empeora por el frío.

Rhus toxicodendron

— Piel roja e hinchada, con erupción vesiculosa quemante y pruriginosa.

— Picor intenso que no se alivia por el rascado, pero puede mejorar aplicando agua tan caliente como la pueda soportar.

— Irresistible deseo de moverse o cambiar de posición a cada rato, seguido de gran alivio.

Urtica urens

— Es muy útil en urticarias generalizadas tras la ingestión de marisco.

— Erupción similar a la que producirían las hojas de ortiga.

— Gran picor y ardor, agravados por rascado, frío y baño.

Varicela

Enfermedad eruptiva de origen vírico, benigna, muy contagiosa, que confiere una inmunidad muy sólida.

Puede comenzar sin ninguna sintomatología, o bien con dolor de cabeza, catarro nasal y malestar generalizado. Más tarde presenta pequeñas vesículas pruriginosas, que se abren y dan lugar a la formación de costras. Estas lesiones comienzan en el tronco y después se extienden al resto del cuerpo, incluido el cuero cabelludo.

Como ésta es una enfermedad febril, pueden emplearse los medicamentos recogidos en el capítulo de «Fiebre», así como estos indicados en la erupción:

Antimonium crudum

— Vesículas con líquido espeso y viscoso en su interior, que forman después costras amarillentas. Con intenso picor agravado por el calor.

— Lengua con una capa blanca y espesa, como leche. Sin hambre, pero con sed de bebidas aciduladas.

— Evacuaciones semisólidas.

Mercurius vivus

— Erupción vesiculosa, primero, pustulosa después.

— Lengua con capa amarillenta, que guarda la impresión de los dientes.

— Sudores nocturnos abundantes, viscosos y agotadores. Sed intensa.

Mezereum

— Vesículas ardorosas y muy pruriginosas, rodeadas de un halo rojo y cubiertas por una costra blanquecina, bajo la cual se colecta un líquido amarillento.

Pulsatilla vulgaris.

Pulsatilla

— Vesículas con picor violento, que empeora por el rascado y por el calor de la cama.

— Fiebre sin sed y con escalofríos.

— El niño está mimoso, tímido y llorón. No tolera el calor; quiere destaparse.

Rhus toxicodendron

— Piel roja con erupción vesiculosa que arde y pica. El picor es muy intenso y se agrava por el rascado.

— Muy agitado, se mueve continuamente en la cama buscando un lugar cómodo.

Indice alfabético de remedios homeopáticos descritos en el libro

Indice

BEGINNING UKULELE

The Complete Ukulele Method

Beginning • Intermediate • Mastering

GREG HORNE
SHANA AISENBERG
EDITED BY DANIEL HO

Alfred Music
P.O. Box 10003
Van Nuys, CA 91410-0003
alfred.com

ISBN-10: 0-7390-9548-X (Book & DVD)
ISBN-13: 978-0-7390-9548-5 (Book & DVD)

Photo of Daniel Ho by Larry Lytle
Interior photographs by Greg Horne and Paige M. Travis

CONTENTS

ABOUT THE AUTHORS

Greg Horne is a multi-instrumentalist, songwriter, author, and teacher in Knoxville, Tennessee. He is the author of several books and DVDs published by Alfred Music, including the *Complete Acoustic Guitar Method*, *Teach Yourself Songwriting*, two volumes of the *Complete Mandolin Method*, and the *Couch Potato Guitarist/Bassist* books. Greg holds a bachelor of arts in music from the College of Wooster, and pursued graduate studies at the University of Mississippi. To contact Greg, hear his music, or see his videos, visit: www.greghornemusic.com

Multi-instrumentalist **Shana Aisenberg** plays ukulele, acoustic guitar, lap steel guitar, mandolin, fiddle, banjo, fretted dulcimer, and more. She specializes in American roots styles including fingerpicking blues, slide guitar, bluegrass, old-time flatpicking, swing, and New England contra dance—as well as European folk music styles such as Celtic, klezmer, Balkan, and Scandinavian.

In addition to being a respected author, Shana has recorded, produced, and played on over 50 albums. She has also composed music for films. In 1981, Shana was a triple winner at the prestigious Walnut Valley National Flatpicking Championships, held in Winfield, Kansas, where she placed in the categories of fingerstyle guitar, mandolin, and fretted dulcimer. Shana performs regularly with duo partner Beverly Woods and teaches private lessons and group classes in New Hampshire and online. You can visit Shana on the Web at: www.shanasongs.com

ABOUT THE DVD

VIDEO EXAMPLE The DVD contains valuable demonstrations of the instructional material in this book. You will get the best results by following along with your book as you watch these video segments. The symbol to the left appears next to each song, example, or lesson for which there is an accompanying video demonstration. Example numbers appear above the symbol when applicable. Audio tracks of the musical examples are also included on the DVD for listening and playing along, and they are all accessible on your computer as MP3 files (see DVD-ROM Audio below).

DVD-ROM AUDIO

The accompanying DVD includes MP3 files that are playable on a computer, smartphone, or iPod®*. To access these files, place the disc in the DVD drive of your computer.
Windows users: double-click on My Computer, right-click on your DVD drive icon, select Explore, and then double-click on the DVD-ROM Materials folder.
Mac users: double-click on the DVD icon on your desktop, and then double-click on the DVD-ROM Materials folder.

* iPod is a trademark of Apple Inc.

INTRODUCTION

Aloha! Welcome to *Beginning Ukulele*, the first volume of *The Complete Ukulele Method*, which is a three-volume series designed for ukulele students who are either teaching themselves or working with teachers. These books cover the styles, techniques, and musicianship you need to take your playing as far as you want to go. You have chosen a fun and unique instrument that is becoming more popular than ever. The ukulele is accessible, portable, and sounds great whether you play it simply or with dazzling virtuosity. This book is written to help you have fun and play real music you will love as quickly as possible.

WHO SHOULD USE THIS BOOK?
Beginning Ukulele is written to get you started playing ukulele even if you've never touched an instrument before. The intermediate player can also benefit from this book, using it to brush up on fundamental skills and lay a solid foundation for further development. Players of other fretted instruments will be able to use this book to add the uke to their musical bag of tricks.

WHAT IS IN THIS BOOK?
This book covers basic musical skills that apply to all styles. Some of the skills and concepts you will learn include:
- How to choose, tune, hold, and strum your ukulele
- A bit about uke history and the players that have inspired its popularity
- Strumming basic open chords to accompany songs
- Reading standard music notation and tablature (TAB)
- Strumming styles to accompany old-time fiddle music, traditional jazz, and swing
- The basics of scales and improvising
- The structure of major scales, keys, and chords
- Moveable chord shapes that allow you to play every major, minor, and dominant 7th chord
- Specialized techniques that apply to Hawaiian music, swing, blues, fingerstyle, and rock ukulele

HOW TO USE THIS BOOK
Each chapter in this book contains a group of lessons that are related by a theme or set of skills. The chapters are progressive, meaning each lesson within a chapter builds on the previous lesson. The book is designed so that you can work from the beginning to the end, but it is also possible to skip around and work on multiple chapters simultaneously once you master the basic skills found in Chapters 1 and 2.

WATCH FOR SUPER UKE TIPS!
These highlighted tips will give you secrets to help you practice and acquire new skills.

WHERE DO I GO FROM HERE?
Beginning Ukulele is designed to progress directly to *Intermediate Ukulele*, the second volume in this method. The skills and techniques you learn here will be developed and expanded in the next volume. You will learn more tunes, styles, scales, chords, and improvisation techniques. Happy picking!

CHAPTER 1

Getting Started

LESSON 1: KNOW YOUR UKE

ABOUT THE UKULELE

'Ukulele is a Hawaiian word meaning "jumping flea," alternately translated as "gift that came here." The Hawaiian spelling begins with the *'okina*, which looks like a single quotation mark and signifies a glottal stop (a type of sound used in many spoken languages produced by momentary closure of the glottis followed by a quick release). The Hawaiian pronunciation is "ook-oo-LEH-leh." Many players outside Hawaii pronounce it "you-kuh-LAY-lee," or *uke* for short. The authors of this method acknowledge and respect the ukulele's Hawaiian heritage, but have chosen to use the Anglicized spelling without the *'okina*.

There are a few theories on how the ukulele got its name, including that the player's hand leaps like a "jumping flea" across the strings. The uke began its journey in the Portuguese archipelago of Madeira. The construction of the ukulele is based on the Portuguese *machete*, a relative of the *cavaquinho* and guitar. The *machete* was enormously popular in 19th-century Madeira. Madeirans were recruited for work in Hawaii in the late 1800s. Three luthier/cabinet makers, Manuel Nunes (1843–1922), Jose do Espirito Santo (1850–1905), and Augusto Dias (1842–1915) arrived in 1879. In the 1880s, they began building instruments in Honolulu. Soon, the tiny *machete* acquired the tuning of its larger sibling, the *rajão* (which would evolve into the Hawaiian *taropatch*), and became the ukulele.

A renaissance of traditional Hawaiian music, poetry, and dance was blossoming under King Kalakaua (1836–1891) and his sister Queen Liliuokalani (1838–1917) at that time. They both loved the ukulele and helped create the repertoire and popularity that made it synonymous with Hawaiian culture. The best ukuleles were built of koa (*Acacia koa*), a native Hawaiian wood.

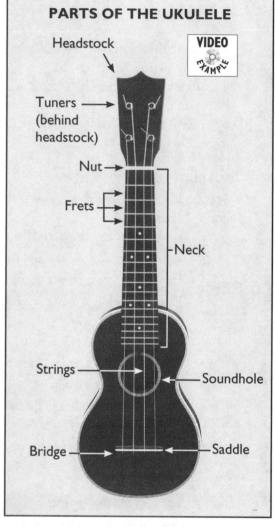

PARTS OF THE UKULELE

VIDEO EXAMPLE

Headstock

Tuners (behind headstock)

Nut

Frets

Neck

Strings

Soundhole

Bridge

Saddle

The ukulele had been heard on the mainland but it really became a hit at the 1915 Panama Pacific International Exhibition in San Francisco. This sparked a uke craze that plowed through the 1920s with musical shows, traveling bands, sheet music, and thousands of ukes sold by catalogs and top builders like Martin. Virtuoso performers like Roy Smeck, Cliff "Ukulele Ike" Edwards, and later England's George Formby kept the uke visible through films and records.

The popularity and "cool factor" of the uke has waxed and waned several times since then. There was a boom in the '50s when TV star Arthur Godfrey inspired the sales of millions of mass-produced plastic ukes. The late '60s saw a revival of Tin Pan Alley uke songs from artists like Tiny Tim and Ian Whitcomb. From the '70s onward, the uke has enjoyed unparalleled diversity through players like Herb "Ohta-San" Ohta, Gordon Mark, Lyle Ritz, and many others.

Now, nearly 100 years after the "Frisco Exhibition," the ukulele is in a new golden age thanks to school programs, internet videos, and virtuosos like Jake Shimabukuro and James Hill. You could be next! For more about the players of the past and present, look for their pictures in this book. Also, see page 96 for excellent reference sources on uke history.

TYPES OF UKULELES

There are four basic types of four-string ukuleles, from smallest to largest: *soprano*, *concert* (sometimes called *alto*), *tenor*, and *baritone*. The soprano, concert, and tenor sizes can be tuned identically (see *Tuning* on page 9), and any of these three sizes can be used with all three books of *The Complete Ukulele Method*. (Note: The baritone uke is tuned differently, like the first four strings of a guitar, and should not be used with this method.)

| Soprano | Concert (Alto) | Tenor | Baritone |

THE BANJO UKE

The *banjo uke* has a four-string ukulele neck (usually around concert size) on a banjo body. These can be tuned and played just like the other uke types. There are also many multi-string variations of the ukulele, including instruments such as the *taropatch ukulele,* the *tiple*, and the *liliu*. Much of the material in this method can be adapted to these instruments, but it's best to start with a four-string uke or banjo uke.

Banjo Ukulele.

WHICH SIZE?

Which ukulele should you start with? It's purely a matter of preference and comfort. If there is a good selection available to you, pick up several and see how they feel. The most common, and least expensive, is the soprano size. You can do everything in this book with a soprano uke. Ukulele virtuosos often play concert and tenor sizes because they afford more room for intricate fingerwork and a fuller tone. At any rate, try to buy your first uke from a seller that has experience and can point you to a quality instrument. Some inexpensive ukes are great, and others have tuning or stability problems that make for later headaches. The uke from the gift shop on the beach may not give you the lifetime of enjoyment you seek!

VIDEO EXAMPLE HOLDING THE UKULELE

Most ukuleles are so small and light they can easily be played sitting or standing without a strap. The most stable position is seated, with the lower bout of the uke resting on the right leg. Use the right forearm to gently hold the uke to the body. Another variation is to hold the uke farther up on the stomach, cradled in the crook of the right arm. Players who are using their thumb exclusively will often support the upper bout of the uke with their right-hand fingers. For unrestricted access to the most advanced techniques, you may find a strap helpful. A strap supports the instrument without restricting the placement of the hands, and also allows you to rock out on stage without fear. Many ukes do not come with strap buttons to attach the strap, but you can get them installed easily and cheaply at a repair shop.

Correct sitting position.

Correct standing position.

PLAYING THE OPEN STRINGS

When you hold the uke with the soundhole facing forward, the string closest to the floor is called the *1st string*. Without touching the strings with your left-hand fingers, try plucking the 1st string with your right-hand thumb or index finger. You don't have to dig deeply into the strings or pull hard on them. Just go for a "medium gentle" level of sound. Move to the next string (away from the floor)—this is the *2nd string*. Then try the *3rd string*. The string closest to your head is the *4th string*. If you're not out of strings yet, you may not have the right instrument for this book!

ABOUT THE 4TH STRING

In the standard tuning used in this book (see *TUNING, next page*), the 1st string is the highest-sounding open note (an A). The 2nd string is lower, an E. The 3rd string is lower, a C. So, the pattern is that the notes get lower as you go from the 1st to 3rd strings. The 4th string breaks the pattern. It is higher in pitch, sounding a G note between the A of the 1st string and the E of the 2nd string. This type of tuning is called a *reentrant tuning* (pronounced "re-entrant"). The 4th string in this tuning is sometimes called the *reentrant string*.

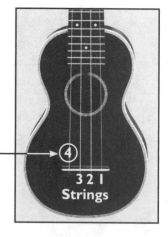

"LOW G" TUNING

There is another popular and useful tuning called "Low G" tuning, in which the 4th string is tuned an octave lower than the reentrant tuning, to a G below the C of the 3rd string. This tuning expands the range of the instrument and increases the options for scales and melodies. This tuning can be easier for guitar players to adapt to, as it is similar to the tuning of the first four strings of a guitar capoed at the 5th fret. For more information, see the Appendix about Low G tuning at the end of this book.

Take a few minutes to play on the different open strings. Take the uke down the hall and show your pets and relatives what you can do. The big time is just around the corner!

TUNING

The Complete Ukulele Method uses the most common standard tuning for the soprano, concert, and tenor ukulele: the G–C–E–A tuning with a high (or "reentrant") G. This will allow you to work through most of the examples in this series with one uke. This tuning is also called "C" or "C6" tuning, because the open notes form a C6 chord (you'll learn what this means later). The first step in tuning is to memorize the names of the open-string notes in standard tuning. The names come from letters in the *music alphabet* (coming up in a few pages). For now, just memorize the letters and which strings they go to (see above).

Tuning a stringed instrument for the first time is not easy. You might prefer to enlist an experienced helper at first. Tuning is a skill that involves listening closely and learning to match pitches exactly. The strings can be tuned by matching them to the tuning notes in the video. An electronic tuner or tuning app on your mobile device can also be very handy. Following are a few other methods you can use to tune.

OPEN STRINGS/NOTES				
String:	4	3	2	1
Note:	**G**	**C**	**E**	**A**

You can make up a sentence for the letters, like:
Grizzly **C**owboys **E**at **A**lone

THE "MATCHING FRETS" METHOD

Step 1: Tune the 1st string to exactly match an A note (also known as A440) on a reference device like a tuner, piano, or pitch pipe.

Step 2: Play your newly tuned A string and listen to the note. Now play the 5th fret on the 2nd string and compare it to the open 1st string. Tune the 2nd string so that the pitch of the 5th fret exactly matches the pitch of the open 1st string. It's okay to play a string and let it ring while you turn the tuning machine. This can help you judge how far to go.

Step 3: Play your newly tuned E string (2nd string) open and listen to the note. You will then tune the 3rd string (C string) so that the 4th fret note exactly matches the open 2nd string.

Step 4: To tune the 4th string, play the 3rd fret on the 2nd string. This step is a little different because you're going to use the fretted note as the reference. Tune the 4th string (G) so that it exactly matches the 3rd fret of the 2nd string.

FOR GUITAR PLAYERS ONLY

The tuning of the uke is very similar in interval structure to the tuning of the guitar. Imagine the first four strings of the guitar (D–G–B–E, from low to high) capoed or barred at the 5th fret, giving the notes G–C–E–A (low to high). Now, imagine the 4th string replaced with a thinner string and tuned up an octave. This is uke tuning. If you're a guitar player, you'll recognize many chord shapes and scale formations, but they will have different names due to the different tuning.

THE PIANO OR KEYBOARD METHOD

You can tune to a piano by matching the strings to the keys shown.

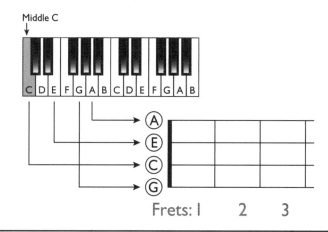

THE LEFT-HAND POSITION

The key to a good left-hand position is to keep your thumb behind the neck, resting lightly and allowing the palm to be open. The position that affords the most agility with the least strain is a guitar-style grip with the pad of the thumb near the center of the back of the neck and the palm completely open. Your fingers should be curved. If you are coming to the uke from playing violin or mandolin, you can modify a position that cradles the neck between the thumb and the side of the lowest joint of the index finger. In this position, the fingers may be angled slightly to reach higher frets. Try not to hold up the weight of the neck with your left hand. Use a strap or sit so the uke is supported.

Guitar-style grip.   *Mandolin-style grip.*

FRETTING AND PLAYING NOTES

To fret a note, place your finger just to the left of the fret you want to play, and press the string down so that it makes solid contact with the fret. Pluck the string with your right-hand index finger or thumb. Do not press down directly on top of the fret, as your finger will mute the string. Keep the pressure steady for as long as you want the note to ring. It helps to remember: *the fret makes the note, the finger gets the string to the fret.*

LEFT-HAND FINGERS

Your left-hand fingers are numbered as follows:

Index = 1
Middle = 2
Ring = 3
Pinky = 4

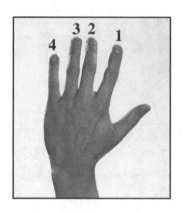

A HIDDEN SOURCE OF DIFFICULTY

The most important factors for a long life of playing are to keep the fingers curved and the hand muscles as relaxed as possible. A spot to watch out for is the muscle group at the joint of the thumb and the hand. Often, these muscles will become tense and squeeze together when you are concentrating while practicing—you may not even know it's happening! It may also happen if you are holding up the neck with your hand. This is a source of tension in your hand that can cause fatigue and difficulty. Check on it often and consciously relax this muscle group until it learns to stay that way.

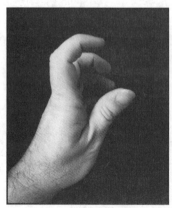
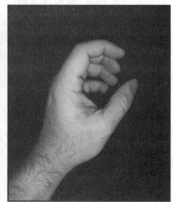

Bad, tense, ouch!   *Good, open, relaxed.*

READING WHATLATURE?

Tablature, called *TAB* for short, is a system of writing music for fretted string instruments. It tells you what fret to play and what string to play it on.

The long horizontal lines represent the strings. The top line is the 1st string (A), and the bottom line is the 4th string (G). The numbers indicate which fret to play. Underneath the TAB you'll see a row of numbers that indicate which left-hand finger to use for each note. Try fingering the notes indicated below.

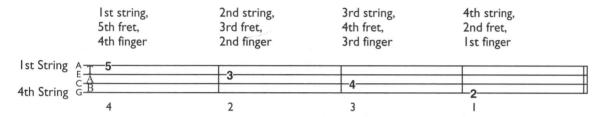

| | 1st string, 5th fret, 4th finger | 2nd string, 3rd fret, 2nd finger | 3rd string, 4th fret, 3rd finger | 4th string, 2nd fret, 1st finger |

SUPER UKE TIP

The dots, or fret markers, on your ukulele neck will help you keep track of the frets (especially as you get up high on the neck). Dots are commonly found marking frets 5, 7, 10, and 12. Soprano ukes often have necks that join the body at the 12th fret, so this fret may not be marked. There are variations in the position markers used on ukes, so be sure to familiarize yourself with your own uke!

TAB is often attached to written music known as *standard music notation*, so the player will know how long the notes last and when they occur. Standard music notation is introduced in Chapter 3, and as you become accustomed to reading it, it will become more and more helpful. The following tune shows TAB and standard music notation. If you do not read music yet, do not panic. Just play the frets and strings indicated in a slow, steady rhythm, giving each note an equal amount of time. You may recognize the tune.

VIDEO EXAMPLE — *MARY HAD A BORDER COLLIE*

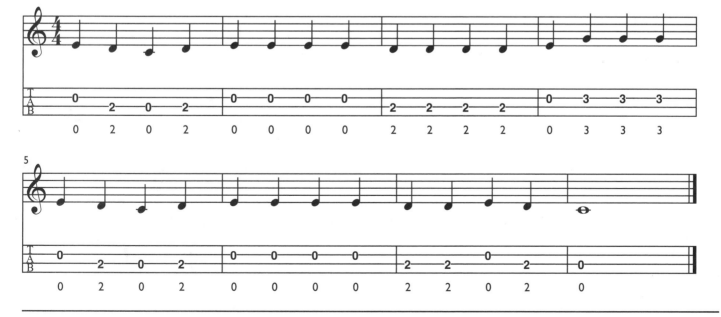

LESSON 3: THE NOTES ON THE FRETBOARD

VIDEO The trick to learning the notes on the fretboard is understanding the musical alphabet. You only need to remember four things to master the musical alphabet:

I. The musical alphabet goes from A to G, then starts over again with A:

A B C D E F G A B C and so on

This series of seven notes, called *natural notes,* repeats in a continuous cycle. As you move forward through the alphabet, the notes get higher in pitch. When moving through the series, each note can be called a *step*.

2. Steps come in two sizes: *half steps* **(I fret) and** *whole steps* **(2 frets).**

The closest one note can be to another on the ukulele is the distance of one fret. This one-fret distance is called a *half step*. The distance of two frets (or two half steps) is called a *whole step*. For example, from the 1st fret to the 2nd fret is a half step, while the distance from the 1st to the 3rd fret is a whole step.

Half step   =   One fret
Whole step   =   Two frets

3. In the musical alphabet, all letters are a whole step apart except B to C and E to F (which are each a half step apart.)

B to C is a half step
E to F is a half step

Below is the musical alphabet from A to A with each block representing a half step, or one fret.

Musical Alphabet (Showing Natural Notes Only)

A		B	C		D		E	F		G		A

4. Special symbols called *accidentals* **are used to name the notes between the natural notes. Remember, there are no notes between B and C or E and F.**

MEET THE ACCIDENTALS		
Symbol	Name	Description
♯	Sharp	A *sharp* raises a natural note by one half step (one fret). For example, the note one half step above A is called "A sharp" (A♯).
♭	Flat	A *flat* lowers a natural note by one half step (one fret). For example, the note one half step below B is called "B flat" (B♭).
♮	Natural	A *natural* returns a sharp or flat note to its original, natural position. Notes are assumed to be natural unless a flat or sharp is indicated. You can call the A note "A natural," or just "A."

All sharp notes can have a flat name, and all flat notes can have a sharp name. In other words, each note that is in-between two natural notes has two names, a sharp name and a flat name. The note between A and B can be called A♯ or B♭, and both names fall on the same fret. Two notes that have different names but the same sound are called *enharmonic equivalents*.

THE CHROMATIC SCALE

The music alphabet, with all the half steps included, is called the *chromatic scale*. It has 12 half steps. In other words, if you start on A, the 13th note you reach will be A again. Each repetition of the same note in the cycle is called an *octave*. This is because the cycle contains only seven distinct letters, so the eighth letter you reach will be the one you started with.

Here is the music alphabet, or chromatic scale, again. Can you fill in the missing note names? Check the 1st string on the chart at the bottom of the page to see how you did.

A	A♯ B♭	B	C	___	D	___	E	F	___	G	___	A

Practice naming the notes of the chromatic scale forward *and* backward (using both sharp and flat names) until you can do it perfectly every time.

REVIEWING THE OPEN STRINGS

The strings of your ukulele are tuned to the following pitches:

Note:	G	C	E	A
String:	4	3	2	1

If you haven't yet, memorize the notes of the open strings: **G**rizzly **C**owboys **E**at **A**lone!

Now that you know the music alphabet and the open strings, pick any string and try to name the notes starting from open. Below are all the notes on the ukulele from the open string to the 12th fret. Note that the 12th fret brings you back to the note name you started with for that string. The 12th fret marks the octave of the open string, so we say that the neck "starts over" at the 12th fret.

All the Notes on the Ukulele Fretboard

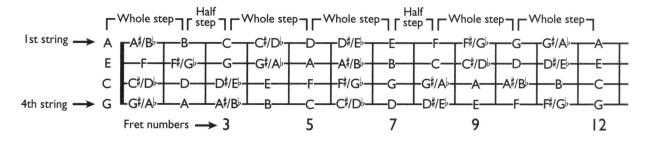

CHAPTER 2

Strum, Strum, Strum

With just a few chords and a bit of know-how, you can make some real music right away. A *chord* is three or more notes sounded simultaneously. The way to remember that is a *note* is one sound at a time (like one person singing), and a *chord* is a bunch of notes played or sung together. Your first chords are called *open chords* because they involve a mixture of *open* (unfingered) strings and fretted notes.

SUPER UKE TIP
During this phase of your learning, it is more important to practice often than to practice for long periods of time. Play for a while, then put the uke down and come back to it again later (but not days and days later!).

Muscle memory is what gives us the ability to perform a complex action (like walking) without having to plan it out every time. Muscle memory builds through cycles of repetition, then rest, then returning to repeat the motion again. Give yourself the patience, persistence, and time to let your fingers learn how to master each new skill.

VIDEO STRUMMING

Strum setup.

One of the most common ways to play a chord is to *strum*. You can strum with a pick, fingers, or thumb. Many uke players do most of their strumming using the index, middle, or ring finger—all of which carry the added bonus of being hard to misplace or send through the clothes dryer (unlike a pick).

To strum with a finger (of your strumming hand), start with your hand held near the place where the neck joins the body, with your finger above the 4th string. In one motion, rapidly move your finger across all the strings, striking them all (see photos to the right). It should sound like you hit them all at the same time. It may feel like flicking the back of your fingernail across the strings, or like flicking your hand from the wrist, or a bit of both. Stay very loose and relaxed and practice this several times on the open strings.

Strum follow-through.

Strumming symbols:

 *Downstroke*
(strum toward the floor)

V *Upstroke*
(strum toward the ceiling)

SUPER UKE TIP
The best basic uke tone is produced by strumming the strings somewhere between the soundhole and the neck joint (where the neck meets the body). Find the spot that is comfortable and sounds good to you, and use this spot as "home base" most of the time. Next, try moving toward the headstock where the sound gets softer and sweeter, and then toward the bridge where the sound gets louder, brighter, and, eventually, more nasal or metallic. It's your uke. Go nuts.

READING CHORD DIAGRAMS

Chords, like notes, are named after letters in the music alphabet, sometimes with additional words or numbers to describe the chord better. The chords you will learn first are called *major* chords, which denotes a special sound and structure you'll learn about soon. Usually, a chord is assumed to be major unless stated otherwise, so it's not necessary to indicate it verbally or in the music. For instance, a "C" chord is understood as C Major, a "G" chord as G Major, etc.

The tuning of the uke produces a very nice chord using just the open strings, called C6 ("C six.") To play other chords, you'll need the fingers of your fretting hand. Chords are most often shown using *chord diagrams*. A chord diagram is like a picture of the fretboard that shows which strings, fingers, and frets are used to make the chord. To the right is a diagram for a C chord, with a little tour to show you around.

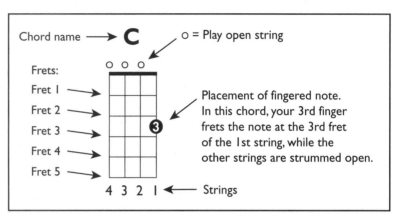

READING A CHORD CHART

You can learn songs using *chord charts* written in *slash notation*. The chord chart shows which chords to play and when to change them. Each slash indicates one beat in a steady rhythm. The *beat* is the steady pulse of the music. Imagine marching military style, counting steps 1, 2, 3, 4, with each step in the same rhythm. That's the same as keeping a beat in music. The beats in the example below are grouped in *measures* (or *bars*) of four beats. Vertical *bar lines* mark the measures. The *final double bar line* at the end indicates that the song is over and it's time to get a drink. Try strumming this example using your C chord. Keep a steady beat by counting out loud and strumming at the same time.

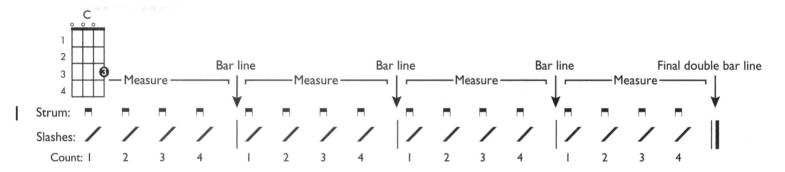

Here's another one that lets you switch between your C chord and the C6 chord made by the open strings. Switch to C6 in measure 3. The two dots before the double bar tell you to repeat the song.

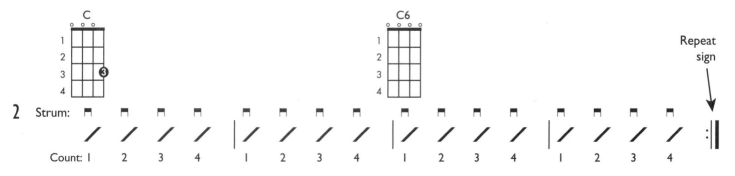

NEW CHORDS: F AND G7

Below is a reminder for C and C6, and, also, two new chords to try: F and G7. The F chord uses two fingers, and the G7 uses three. Practice making them over and over, and switching between them. Strum them normally, but also remember to pick each string individually to make sure all the notes in the chord ring out. Sometimes, you'll find one of your fingers is touching an open string, or that a bad note is hiding among the good ones. (Bad notes are sneaky.)

VIDEO EXAMPLE

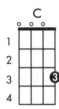 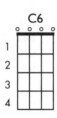 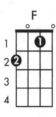 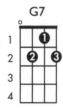

It might help to talk through each chord diagram out loud, one string at a time. For instance:

For the G7 chord, you have:
1st string, 3rd finger, 2nd fret
2nd string, 1st finger, 1st fret
3rd string, 2nd finger, 2nd fret
4th string, open

TOTALLY AWESOME PRACTICE STRATEGIES FOR LEARNING NEW CHORDS

The "Squeeze and Relax" Trick

A great way to help get a new chord shape into your muscle memory is to try these steps.

1. Form the chord as perfectly as you can, making sure all the notes ring out.
2. Instead of moving on to another chord, just relax the pressure of your fingers *without lifting them off the string*. This gives you a rest from squeezing but lets you stay on the same chord.
3. After relaxing the pressure for a second or two, press the notes back down ("squeeze") and strum the chord again. Beware that fingers may have shifted slightly between squeezings and you may have to correct their positions.
4. Repeat the squeeze/strum and relax steps several times before changing chords. You won't notice a big difference right away, but each time you revisit the chord with this process, it will get easier and easier.

Switching Chords in Pairs and the Two-Pronged Strategy

Once the individual chords start to get easier, you can begin to work on switching them in pairs. Start with C and F. A good strategy is to use two different types of practicing:

- *Slow Motion Practicing:* Play the first chord, then figure out where each finger needs to go for the second chord. Practice going back and forth slowly, without rhythm, teaching your fingers to move together to the new chord.
- *Practicing in Rhythm:* After you've done the slow motion practice for a few minutes, try counting a slow, steady beat and play two measures of each chord as shown on the next page. Repeat the progression over and over so that you practice switching both to and from the new chord.
- *Use both approaches each time you practice!* Even though it won't be smooth at first, you'll see improvement over a few practice sessions with this two-pronged approach and a bit of patience. You can work on several pairs of chords in each practice session. It will keep you from getting bored with just two chords, and before long, you'll be switching like a pro.

Following are three pairs of chords you can practice. Usually, a repeat sign means "repeat just once," but you should repeat these examples several times. Treat each example like it is a longer song made of just two chords. Count out loud so you know exactly when to change chords.

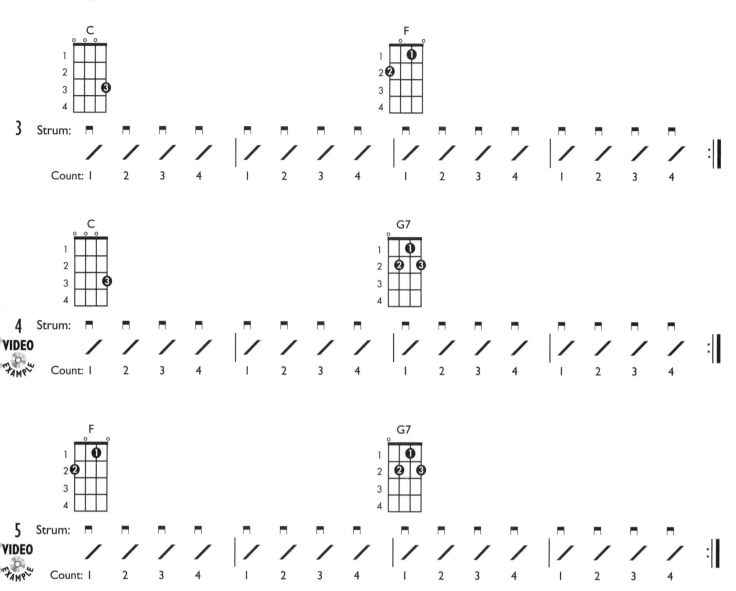

When you have the two-chord examples above going fairly smoothly, try this progression using all four chords.

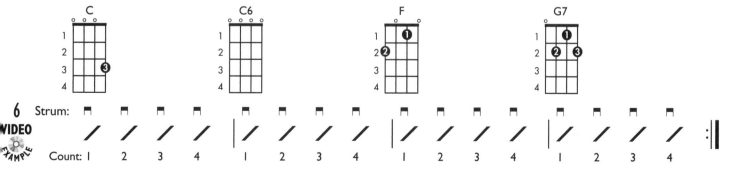

Here are a couple of full-sized songs you can use to practice your C, F, and G7 chords and your strumming. It might help to count the beats out loud the first few times through. Then, later, you can try adding the words. In these songs, the words can be sung on the same beats you strum, though not every strum is going to have a word. Soon you'll be able to loosen up the phrasing of the words, while still keeping a steady beat with the strums.

VIDEO EXAMPLE *OH! SUSANNA*

Stephen Foster
(1826–1864)

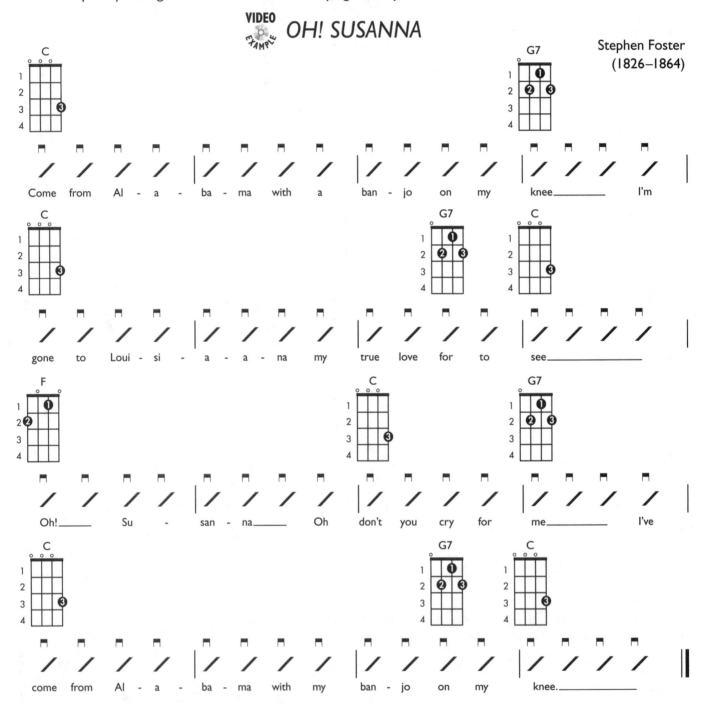

Come from Al - a - ba - ma with a ban - jo on my knee_____ I'm

gone to Loui - si - a - a - na my true love for to see_____

Oh!_____ Su - san - na_____ Oh don't you cry for me_____ I've

come from Al - a - ba - ma with my ban - jo on my knee._____

WHAT KEY ARE WE IN?

Both of the songs in this lesson are in the key of C. The *key* of a song is named after the note or chord upon which the music *resolves,* or comes to rest, called the *tonic note* or *tonic chord.* Songs don't always begin on the tonic chord, but they often end on it. Imagine that a passage of music is like going on a walk and a key is like a neighborhood. The tonic note or chord is like "home." You may go away from home and come back many times, but eventually you are likely to return home and stay. In these songs, "home" is the C chord. You can test this by playing the song, and then trying one of the other chords at the end. In the key of C, only the C chord will make the song sound finished or complete.

WHEN THE SAINTS GO MARCHING IN

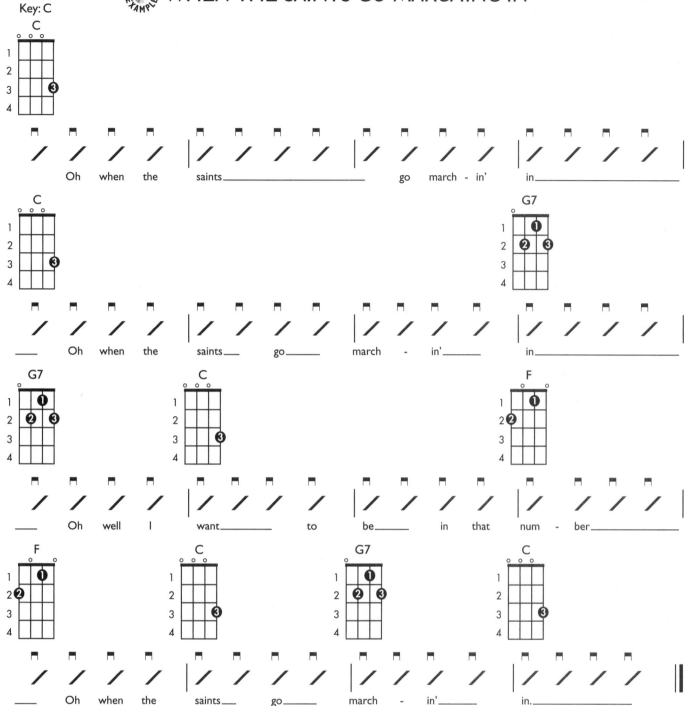

Key: C

Oh when the saints_____ go march - in' in_____

Oh when the saints___ go___ march - in'_____ in_____

Oh well I want_____ to be___ in that num - ber_____

Oh when the saints___ go___ march - in'_____ in._____

TIPS FOR PLAYING AND SINGING

Notice in this song that the first word is on beat 2 of the bar. This is true for each of the four lines. When you play and sing, sometimes you'll play and sing together; other times you'll be strumming without words to keep the beat. If you count out the measures and study the music, you'll always know what beat to come in on.

*In recent years, the ukulele has become an instrument of choice for songwriters and performers who share their music through Internet video sites like YouTube. **Julia Nunes** (b. 1989) began posting songs from her room at home in 2007. Her originals and distinctive covers have generated millions of views.*

LESSON 4: SPICE UP YOUR STRUMMING

Now that you are comfortable with at least a few basic chords and can keep a steady beat, you can shift your attention from your left hand to your right hand and begin refining your strumming technique.

Here are some things to keep in mind when working on your strumming:

- Keep your wrist loose and your arm and fingers relaxed. This is a hallmark of ukulele style!

- Resist the urge to tighten up your muscles as you play faster. Slow the beat down so you can stay relaxed.

SUPER UKE TIP

To become a truly good uke player, you must develop an internal sense of rhythm that is steady and predictable. The best way to do this is to tap your foot on the beats and count out loud. Practice slowly and synchronize the movements of your right hand with the tapping and counting. As you get better, work with a metronome (see page 95) to further solidify your beat.

RHYTHMIC NOTATION

The following examples introduce *rhythmic notation*. This is a common way to show strumming rhythms when a specific rhythm is called for, without having to show every note of the chord. Rhythmic notation differs from standard notation (see Chapter 3) in that the note values are indicated with slashes or diamond shapes instead of circles.

QUARTER NOTES

You've already learned that the beat is the steady pulse that remains constant throughout a passage of music, and that beats are grouped into measures. You've been playing in measures of four beats, which is such a common division of beats that it is known as *common time*. In common time, each beat of the four beats is one quarter of the whole measure, so we call all notes that last one beat *quarter notes* (even when they're not in common time).

Quarter Note

SIGNS OF THE TIMES: THE TIME SIGNATURE

At the beginning of a piece of music, you will see what looks like a fraction. This is a *time signature*. The top number 4 indicates four beats per measure. The bottom number 4, like a fraction, can be understood as "fourths" or "quarters." The $\frac{4}{4}$ time signature means "four quarter note beats in every measure." Sometimes, $\frac{4}{4}$ is shown as $\mathbb{C}$ for "common time."

Time Signature

PLAYING QUARTER NOTES

Below are two bars of quarter notes in rhythmic notation. Play a C chord just as if the quarter notes were slashes.

EIGHTH NOTES

If you divide a quarter note into two equal pieces, you get *eighth notes*. In notation, a single eighth note looks like a quarter note with a flag attached to the stem. When eighth notes appear in groups (often in groups of two or four), they can be *beamed* together. In counting, we want to preserve the same beat and counts we used for quarter notes, so we insert the word "and" in between the numbers to indicate the second possible eighth note of each beat. ("One and two and three and four and," or "1 & 2 & 3 & 4 &.")

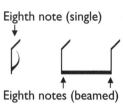

Eighth note (single)

Eighth notes (beamed)

STRUMMING EIGHTH NOTES

When strumming eighth notes, strum down on all numbered beats and up (away from the floor) on all the "&'s." This will get you moving in a steady, alternating down-up motion that you will use to learn new strums. It will probably work best to use your right-hand index finger to strum both down and up. Here are two measures of eighth notes for you to count and strum. Note the repeat sign!

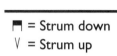

◼ = Strum down
V = Strum up

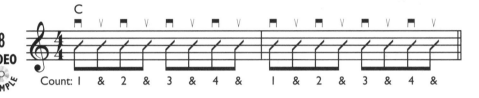

8

Count: 1 & 2 & 3 & 4 & 1 & 2 & 3 & 4 &

SUPER UKE TIP

Repeat this sentence to yourself and make it your rule for strumming:

  "Down on the numbers, up on the 'ands!'"

Use this rule even if you are playing quarter notes and not hitting the strings on the "&." You can tap your foot the same way. Tap down on the number and move the foot up on the "&."

MIXING IT UP

Below is a great sounding strum for lots of songs. You'll want to practice this one over and over with all of your chords until it feels natural. Make sure you keep the eighth notes equal in length; it's easy for them to become uneven.

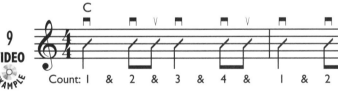

9

Count: 1 & 2 & 3 & 4 & 1 & 2 & 3 & 4 &

Note that it helps to count the "&'s" that are part of the quarter notes even though you're not playing them. This will keep your rhythm more steady and will remind you to move your hand up on the "&" so you will be ready for the next down.

When you're comfortable with the example above, go back to the songs in the previous lesson and apply this strum pattern to each measure.

VIDEO EXAMPLE INTRODUCING G, D, D7, A, AND A7

You've already learned G7—now you can learn G, which, coincidentally, looks like G7 upside down on the fretboard. G is a simpler sounding major chord and can be used in place of G7 in many circumstances.

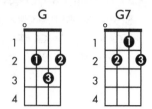

The D chord is shown with two fingerings. Many chords can be played in different ways depending on the needs of the situation. Start with a fingering that works for you, then learn other fingerings later. The second fingering of D uses the 1st finger across three strings to make a *barre* (see page 66). To make a barre, you have to use the flat underside of your finger instead of the tip. D7 is also shown with two fingerings.

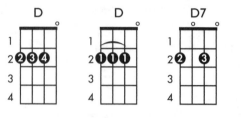

To the right are the A and A7 chords. A7 has two fingerings. As with D7 above, the two fingerings actually produce different arrangements of the notes in an A7 chord, so they are referred to as different *voicings*.

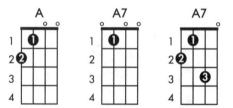

Here's a practice song you can use to work on your new chords. This song uses D, G, A, and A7, and is in the key of D. Notice how the music comes to rest on the tonic chord of D at the end. You can also try using the alternate fingerings for D or A7 shown above.

VIDEO EXAMPLE *MY DEAR, DEAR MAMA FROM MADEIRA*

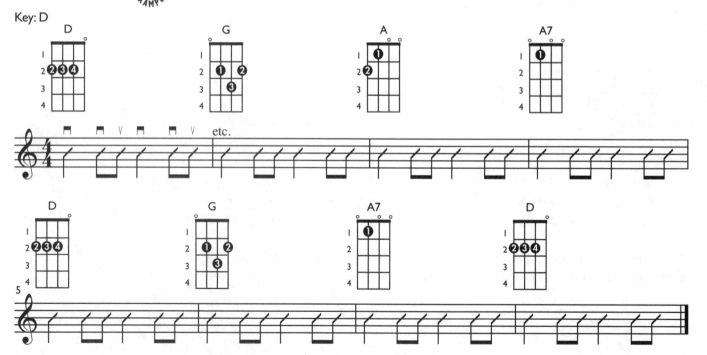

Below are the chords for the traditional Hawaiian song "Wai O Ke Aniani (Crystal Water)." This song is in the key of G. It is popular with players of the *Hawaiian slack-key guitar style*, which involves special tunings and fingerstyle techniques and is sometimes accompanied by ukulele. Slack-key master Gabby Pahinui recorded this song in the 1940s, and many other artists have recorded it since then. "Wai O Ke Aniani" has different melodies for the verse and chorus but the chord progression is the same.

To get even more out of practicing this song, you can also try it with the alternate fingering of D7, or you can play either fingering of the D chord in place of the D7.

VIDEO EXAMPLE — WAI O KE ANIANI (CRYSTAL WATER)

Key: G

Traditional Hawaiian

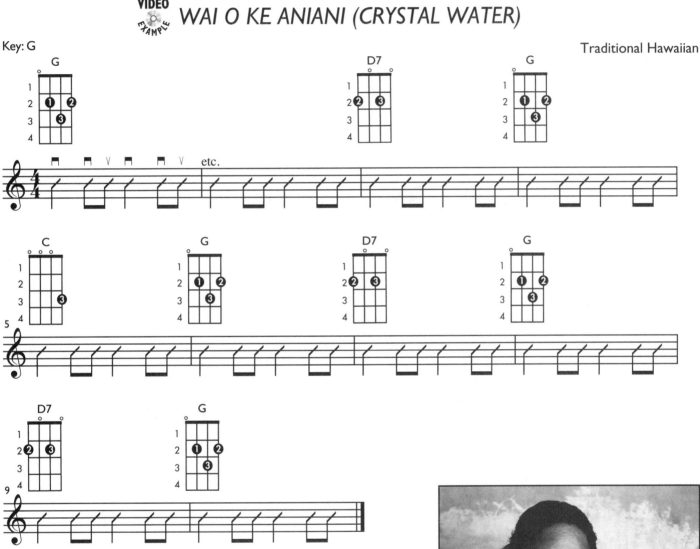

Israel "IZ" Kamakawiwoʻole (1959–1997) was known to his fans as "Bruddah Iz." He inspired new interest in ukulele music with his 1993 interpretation of "Over the Rainbow/ What a Wonderful World," which became a worldwide hit in the 2000s. In 1976, Iz co-founded the Makaha Sons of Niʻihau, a band focused on bringing traditional Hawaiian music to a modern audience. Iz was much beloved for his tenor voice and tireless devotion to preserving Hawaiian cultural memory and independence through music.

The chords you have learned so far are called "major" chords. They can be described as having a bright, happy sound because of the way the notes relate to each other. As you have seen, chord symbols for major chords are simply the letter name of the root. Any chord that is marked *min* is a *minor* chord. Minor chords have a darker or sadder emotional quality. You will learn more about the structures that create these sounds later.

Below are the minor chords that can be played in *open position* on the ukulele. (Open position refers to the open strings plus the first four frets.) In the case of Cmin, the first fingering is more common; the second fingering is shown if you have trouble barring your finger at first. To play the second fingering for Cmin, you have to mute the 2nd string (indicated by the "x"). You can do this by leaning your 2nd finger at a slight angle so that part of the finger touches the 2nd string to keep it from ringing. Use whichever Cmin works best for you.

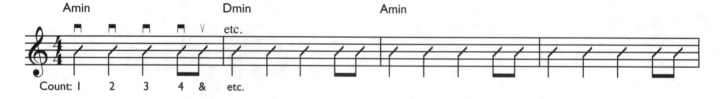

Try "It's Only a Minor Inconvenience" to get familiar with Amin, Dmin, and Emin. You'll notice a couple of new things.

- The chord diagrams are not shown. Many chord charts for songs only show the names of the chords. It's time to make sure you are memorizing new chords so that you know them whether or not the diagram is shown!

- There is a new strum pattern to try: three quarter notes and two eighths (down, down, down, down-up).

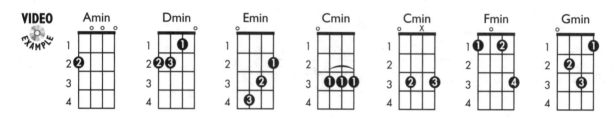

IT'S ONLY A MINOR INCONVENIENCE

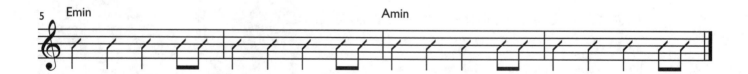

SUPER UKE TIP: IT'S OK TO LEAVE EARLY!

Have you noticed that when you're strumming, it's hard to change to a new chord on time? This is especially true if the strum pattern has an eighth note at the end (on the "&" of 4). Experienced strummers have a way to deal with this. You can lift your left-hand fingers up on the last upstroke in the strum pattern and move toward the new chord. That way you will be able to place your fingers on the new chord at the next downstroke. You will hear your upstroke striking the open strings as your fingers move. This may sound a little strange all by itself, but in the flow of the rhythm, it's so short that it becomes masked by the sound of the real chords. You may want to strum a little lighter on that last upstroke so that the open strings don't get as much emphasis.

Here's what it would look like if we added a diagram for the open chord in the strum you learned on page 24. Think of it not as a distinct chord (technically it's a C6) but as a transition chord.

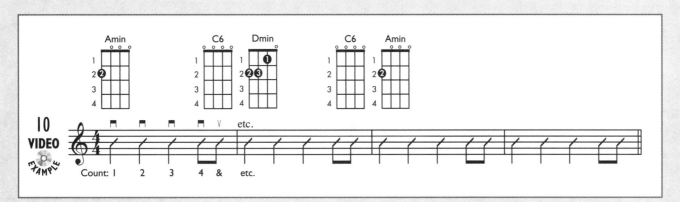

The rule to remember is this: It is more important to get to the next chord on time than it is to hold the current chord through the last eighth note. Of course, if you can do both, that's even better!

Here's one more progression to try using Cmin, Gmin, Dmin, and Fmin. Don't forget your new trick (above) for switching chords on time.

◇ = *Half-note strum*. One strum rings out for two beats.

VIDEO *Waltz time* is another name for $\frac{3}{4}$ time. This means there are three beats in every measure and the quarter note gets one beat. First, familiarize yourself with the feel of three beats per measure by counting and tapping your foot for a few bars.

12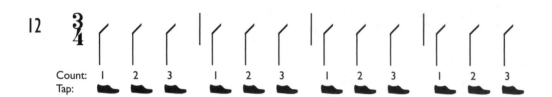

There are a variety of ways to strum in $\frac{3}{4}$ time.

13

VIDEO

Waltz Strum No 1:

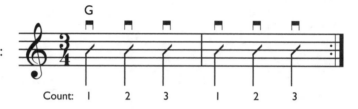

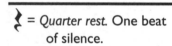 = *Quarter rest.* One beat of silence.

14

VIDEO

Waltz Strum No. 2:

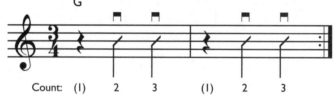

15

VIDEO

Waltz Strum No. 3:

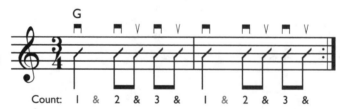

The gentle roll of waltz time can be particularly beautiful and lyrical. One of the most famous songs in $\frac{3}{4}$ is "Amazing Grace." Practice the chords using any of the strums on the previous page. You can also try the melody, which is shown in standard notation and TAB. You may have an easier time learning the melody if you come back to it after you've worked through Chapter 3. This arrangement of "Amazing Grace" is in the key of G. If you need to, you can simplify the chords by playing D instead of D7, and G instead of G7.

PICKUPS

The melody of "Amazing Grace" has two eighth notes before the first full measure. This is called a *pickup*. The two eighth notes that begin "Amazing Grace" are counted as beat 3 of an empty (or count-in) measure. The value of the pickup is then subtracted from the last measure. Sometimes it helps to count a waltz in with two measures. Count "1, 2, 3, 1, 2" and begin playing on beat 3. If you are strumming chords, wait until beat 1 of the first full measure (after the pickup notes) to come in with your strum pattern.

INTRODUCTION TO DOTTED HALF NOTES

Additionally, notice that the melody contains dotted half notes (𝅗𝅥.) in measures 7 and 15. These last for three beats. For more on dotted half notes, see page 34.

VIDEO EXAMPLE AMAZING GRACE

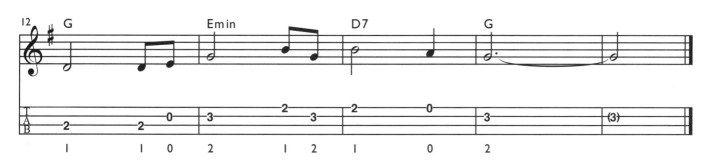

Check out the *Intermediate Ukulele* volume in this method. You'll revisit "Amazing Grace" with alternate chords and learn how to make a solo arrangement of it.

Now that you've had some experience playing the ukulele, it's time to look at the tools we can use to produce different sounds. Here are the main options used by most players:

- Index finger (usually labeled *i*)—using downstrokes and upstrokes
- Thumb (labeled *T*)—using downstrokes and upstrokes
- Combination of *i* and *T*.
- Fingerstyle—using thumb (*T*), index (*i*), middle (*m*), and ring (*a*) fingers.
- Pick—either a guitar-style plastic pick, or a hardened felt ukulele pick. Other materials are available, like wood and leather.
- Some fingerstyle players use a thumbpick and/or fingerpicks so they can achieve the brightness and volume of picks with the agility of fingerstyle.

Fingerstyle.

Thumbpick and fingerpicks.

Guitar-style pick.

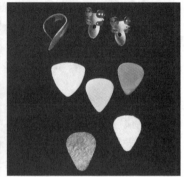
Thumbpick, fingerpicks, guitar picks, and felt ukulele picks.

VIDEO EXAMPLE

HOW TO HOLD A PICK

Place your right-hand thumb across the top of the pick, with the point at a 90-degree angle from your thumb. Then, curve your index finger behind the pick, holding it between your thumb and the side of the first joint of your index finger. Your other fingers can curl into your palm or hang loosely. Just keep them relaxed. If the pick moves around too much when you play, hold it a little closer to the point.

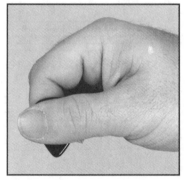
The correct way to hold a pick.

VIDEO EXAMPLE

REST STROKES AND FREE STROKES

There are two main ways to strike a string with the thumb, fingers, or pick. Strumming is usually done with free strokes, while melodies can be played with either free or rest strokes.

Free strokes are the type of strokes you probably have already been using (whether you know it or not). The pick, thumb, or finger strikes the string (or strings) in an uninterrupted motion, either with a downstroke or upstroke. With a free stroke, the string vibrates in a more lateral motion*, roughly parallel to the top.

With a *rest stroke*, the thumb, finger, or pick strikes the string and then comes to rest on the next string that falls in its path (or simulates this motion if there is no string to rest on). Rest strokes cause the strings to vibrate in a motion that is more perpendicular to the top. This transmits more vibration to the bridge and creates a full, round, and sometimes louder tone. Rest strokes with the thumb are used by traditional Hawaiian thumb-style players to get an amazing tone out of the tiny ukulele.

* Technically, the string vibrates in an elliptical or oval pattern that is wider near the middle of the string.

Try any technique you are exposed to. You will find different techniques and tools have different applications in the music you play. Following are the pros and cons of some of the tools discussed in this lesson. Most of this book will work with most styles, though some techniques are more specific.

TOOL	PROS	CONS
Index finger only	• Easy to keep track of • The fingernail gives the downstroke brightness and definition • Can be easily blended with thumb techniques and fingerpicking • Bright sound that projects well	• Can get fatiguing in long, loud jam sessions if you're not careful • Downstroke and upstroke have different tonal qualities due to the fingernail
Thumb only	• Gives a softer, mellower sound with a big, round tone • Thumbnail can add brightness • Easily blended with finger techniques	• Downstroke and upstroke have different tonal qualities due to the thumbnail
Index finger and thumb, or fingerstyle: thumb, index, middle, and ring	• Provides a variety of tonal combinations • Experienced players are able to play with a great deal of speed using the combination of index and thumb • New techniques like triple strums and rolls become possible • See page 88 for more info	• Takes more practice and coordination to get used to • Sacrifices some of the volume and projection that is possible with a pick (in order to gain more tonal color and nuance)
Pick (see below for specific types)	• Easy to strum for long periods of time with a steady, even tone • Upstrokes and downstrokes have very similar tone and projection • Ample volume and bright tone	• More difficult to integrate with finger techniques • Some specialized uke techniques are not possible with a pick
Guitar-style pick (hard plastic or similar)	• Brightest and loudest tone • Readily available • Many shapes, sizes, varieties, and thicknesses • Thin picks make a softer, brighter tone; thick picks make a fuller, louder tone	• Tone may be more brittle or thin sounding than finger/thumb techniques, especially on single notes
Felt "uke" picks	• Made of thick, rigid felt • Softer tone than guitar picks • Over time, the felt becomes more flexible and develops a sound that is similar to strumming with the index finger	• Harder to find in music stores, though still widely available • New picks need some break-in time (keep track of your "good one!")
Thumbpick and/or fingerpicks	• Adds the volume, crisp tone and agility of a pick to the thumb technique • Thumbpick with bare fingers is a good compromise between the pick style and fingerstyle	• Requires quite a bit of practice to become proficient • Fingerpicks, especially the more common metal ones, can sound too bright and harsh on nylon strings

CHAPTER 3

Reading Standard Music Notation

This chapter will provide a quick introduction to reading standard music notation in the 1st position of the ukulele fretboard. You may want to work with this chapter at the same time as you are learning to strum the chords and melodies in Chapters 2 and 5. This will add variety to your practice and keep things interesting. Also, you will be improving in several areas at once, instead of one at a time. Most examples in this chapter do not have tablature, but TAB is used throughout the rest of the book. You do not have to master reading standard music notation in order to work on the other chapters, since TAB is always present.

Reading standard music notation is a rewarding skill that is easier to develop than most people think. It enhances tablature and chord charts by allowing you to read exact rhythms, vocal melodies, and music for other instruments. Even the most basic understanding of the notes of the staff (Lesson 1, below) will give you a point of departure for the concepts introduced later in this book.

LESSON 1: THE NOTES AND THE STAFF

We use five horizontal lines as a sort of playing field for our notes. This is called the *staff*. The *natural notes* (notes without sharps or flats) are placed on the lines and spaces of the staff. Lower notes are near the bottom of the staff, higher notes are near the top. A *clef* sign at the beginning of the staff indicates which notes are represented by which lines and spaces. When the *G Clef* (𝄞) sits on the second line from the bottom of the staff it is called *treble clef*. The line it encircles in the large, lower part of the symbol is called G.

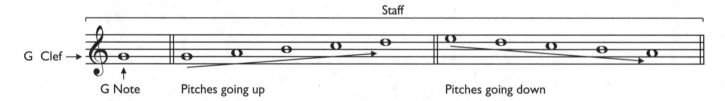

Now that you know the second line from the bottom is G, all the other notes can be related to that line. For example, the space under it is F, the note before G in the musical alphabet. The space above the G line is A, the next note in the musical alphabet.

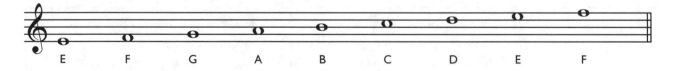

LEARNING THE NOTES ON THE STAFF

If you forget everything else, remember that the G clef encircles the line used for the G note. There are other memory devices you can use to quickly learn all the notes on the staff. One is to separate the notes on the lines from the notes in the spaces. The notes on the lines give you the first letter of each word of this sentence: "**E**very **G**ood **B**eginner **D**oes **F**ine." The notes in the spaces themselves spell the word "**FACE**." Memorize these and you won't get lost on the staff.

Every   Good   Beginner   Does   Fine   F   A   C   E

LESSON 2: THE NATURAL NOTES ON THE 3RD AND 2ND STRINGS

Reading notes on the staff is easier when you learn just a few at a time. Your first notes are on the 3rd and 2nd strings, using your 1st, 2nd, and 3rd fingers. The example below shows where the notes are located on the staff and ukulele. Notice that the C note appears on a *ledger line*. Ledger lines are additional lines that allow us to extend the range of the staff. The D note is in the space below the bottom line of the staff.

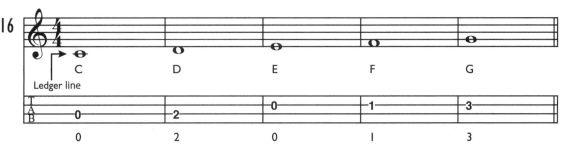

You can play melody notes by plucking them with your thumb or index finger, using either downstrokes or upstrokes. If you are using a pick, play these notes with downstrokes.

As mentioned on the previous page, this chapter will focus on reading notes only on strings 1, 2, and 3. The 4th string is tuned to a high-G note, one whole step below the open A of the 1st string (see About the 4th String on page 8). At first, the 4th string can add a lot of confusion to reading music, since it provides new options for fingering notes found on the first three strings. It is easier if you put off incorporating the 4th string until you can read fluently on the other three. Try the following exercises.

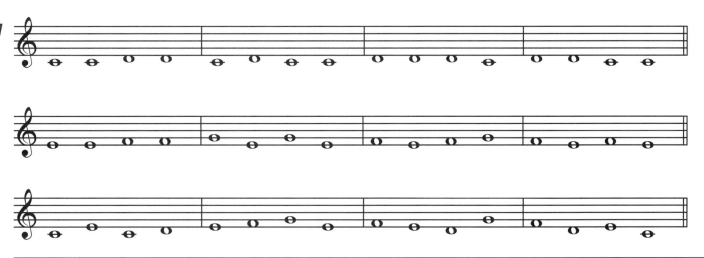

In Chapter 2, you learned a bit about how rhythm is counted and notated. This lesson will review that information as it applies to reading melodies.

BEATS AND MEASURES

The *beat* is the steady, even pulse that remains constant throughout a passage of music. Musicians count beats and divide them into small groups. As you know, a group of beats is called a *measure*. Measures can consist of any number of beats. It is most common to have four beats in a measure. Measures are marked on the staff using *bar lines*. For this reason, measures are also called *bars*. A *double bar* indicates the end of a piece or section.

SIGNS OF THE TIMES

The *time signature* tells you how many beats are in a measure and which type of note will be used to count the pulse of the beat. It is found at the beginning of the piece, or wherever there is a change in time signature within the piece. The upper number indicates the number of beats per measure. The lower number shows what type of note is one beat. The lower number will very often be a 4, indicating that the quarter note (as in the fraction "one fourth") gets one beat.

THE LONG AND SHORT OF IT

The *value* of a note is its duration (in beats). The appearance of a note tells you its value. Following are three note values and their durations.

The *whole note* gets four beats. In a measure of four beats, the whole note lasts for the whole measure. When you play a whole note, make sure it rings for the whole four beats. Counting out loud and tapping your foot to the beat will help. Try these whole notes.

Whole note

The *half note* lasts for two beats, or, half of a measure of four beats. In a four-beat measure, the half notes start on beats 1 and 3. The half note looks like a whole note with a stem. Normally, notes on or above the middle line of the staff have their stems going down, and notes below the middle line have their stems going up.

Half notes

The *quarter note* lasts for one beat. It looks like a half note that has been filled in.

Quarter notes

Try these half-note and quarter-note combinations. Don't forget to count!

> **NOTE ABOUT TEMPO**
> *Division of the measure into whole, half, and quarter notes does not affect the speed of the beat itself. The rate of the beat is called tempo and is expressed in beats-per-minute (bpm). For example, a tempo of ♩ = 60 indicates 60 quarter-note beats per minute, or one beat per second.*

Here is a tune to play using the notes you have learned. Start with a slow tempo and read the rhythm along with the notes. Don't wait until you've learned the notes to figure out the rhythm! By the time you learn just the notes, you may have accidentally made up a new rhythm that you'll have to unlearn. A good approach is to clap or tap out the rhythm of the tune before you even start on the notes.

GO TELL AUNT RHODY

LESSON 4: RESTS

Silence is as important a part of music as sound. The symbols that represent silence are called *rests,* and just like notes, they are divided into wholes, halves, and quarters.

A *whole rest* is four beats of silence. It looks like a small rectangle that hangs like a full suitcase from the fourth line of the staff.

A *half rest* is two beats of silence. It is a small rectangle that sits like a hat on the third line of the staff.

A *quarter rest* is one beat of silence. It looks a bit like a bird flying sideways, if you use your imagination.

> ### SUPER UKE TIP
> *Rests must be "played" with the same precision and intention as pitches. To play a rest, you must stop the string or strings from ringing, either by using your right-hand picking finger or thumb, or by lifting up a fretted note with your left-hand finger to stop the sound.*

The following example uses some of the notes and rests you've learned. Can you play them perfectly?

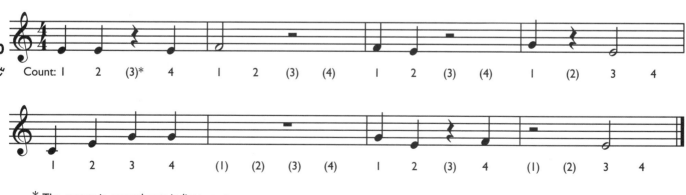

* The counts in parentheses indicate rests.

VIDEO EXAMPLE A *dot* placed after a note head increases its duration by half of the note value. For example, a normal half note lasts for two beats. Half of that value is one beat, so if we add a dot to a half note, it will last for three beats (2 + 1 = 3).

Dotted half note

The traditional song "When the Saints Go Marching In" will give you a chance to work on your notes and rhythms, including quarter rests and dotted half notes. Chords are also shown so you can strum.

VIDEO EXAMPLE *WHEN THE SAINTS GO MARCHING IN*

MORE ABOUT DOTTED NOTES

On page 37, you will learn about dotted quarter notes. Every type of note can be dotted to increase its duration by half of its original value. Even rests can be dotted!

LEGATO AND STACCATO

When you play melodies, each note should last for its full duration. The sound should not stop until the next note (or rest) sounds. This type of note articulation is called legato, *which comes from the Italian for "linked together." Legato is not usually indicated in the music, it is assumed. The alternative to legato is staccato, which means that the notes are detached. Staccato is indicated by dots that appear above or below the note head, opposite the stem. Do not confuse staccato dots with rhythmic dots, which appear to the right of the note head.*

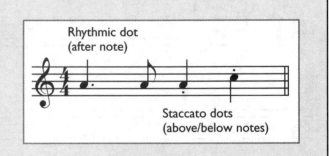

Rhythmic dot
(after note)

Staccato dots
(above/below notes)

LESSON 6: NATURAL NOTES ON THE 1ST STRING

Below are the notes on the 1st string followed by an exercise. (In the exercise, watch out for a note that snuck in from the 2nd string.) Memorize these notes and add them to your collection. You'll be using them all soon!

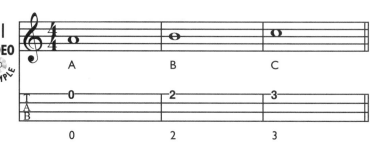

LESSON 7: THE C MAJOR SCALE

A *scale* is a collection of notes used to make melodies and chords. Each scale derives its sound and character from the interval relationships (distances measured in steps) between the tonic note and the other scale notes (for more on intervals, see page 44). The *major scale* has a familiar sound often heard as "Do Re Mi Fa Sol La Ti Do," or in the song "Do-Re-Mi" from *The Sound of Music*.

The major scale has seven notes (eight if you include the return to the tonic note at the end of the scale). It begins on the tonic note, then follows this step pattern to generate the other notes: whole–whole–half–whole–whole–whole–half. By always using this pattern, the major scale can be played in all the keys made possible by the 12 notes of the chromatic scale. In the key of C (using C as the tonic note), the major scale consists of the natural notes—the same notes you have learned in the 1st position of the first three strings. Below is the C Major scale, shown both ascending (going up) and descending (going down), also with the note names and steps.

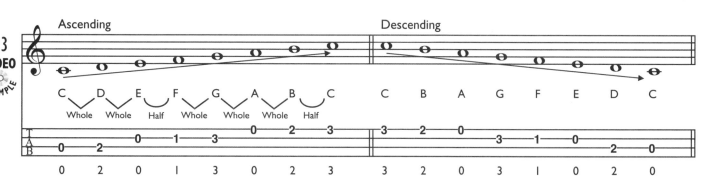

Take some time to practice and memorize the C Major scale. Say the note names out loud, both ascending and descending. What goes up must come down! You should also memorize the formula of steps to make major scales: whole–whole–half–whole–whole–whole–half.

LESSON 8: EIGHTH NOTES (OF COURSE)

As you learned on page 21, the quarter note can be divided into two *eighth notes*, each lasting half of a beat. Single eighth notes have a *flag* attached to the end of the stem opposite the note head. Groups of eighth notes are often *beamed* together. An eighth rest looks like a slash with a small flag waving from it and lasts for half a beat.

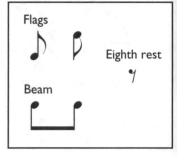

We can organize our note and rest values into a "tree" to help visualize the relationships.

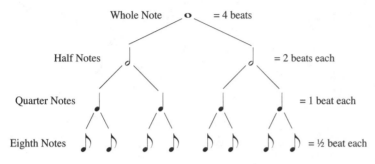

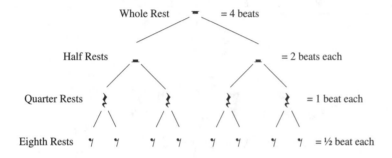

COUNTING EIGHTH NOTES

As you learned on page 21, eighth notes are counted "1 & 2 & 3 & 4 &." The numbered beats are often called *onbeats* or *downbeats,* and the "&'s" are often called *offbeats* or *upbeats.* While counting and playing eighth notes, tap your foot down on the downbeats and move it up on the upbeats.

PLAYING EIGHTH NOTES

When strumming all (or most) of the strings on the uke, it helps to stick with the alternating down-up rhythm you learned on page 21. Remember the Super Uke Tip: "Down on the numbers, up on the &'s!" The way you play eighth notes in single-note melodies depends on the right-hand technique you have chosen.

- If you are used to strumming chords with your index finger or a pick, follow the same "down on the numbers, up on the &'s" motion you would use for strumming chords.

- If you are playing thumb-style, use your thumb (*T*) for downstrokes on the downbeats. Use the index finger (*i*) to play the &'s with upstrokes. If the tempo isn't too fast, you can also use thumb downstrokes on the &'s.

- If you are using your index finger (*i*) in an upstroke, or plucking/fingerpicking motion to play the downbeats, then try using your middle finger (*m*) to play the &'s. This resembles the technique used by classical guitarists and electric bass players.

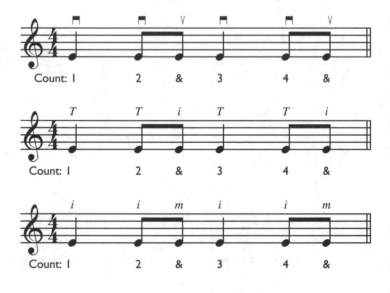

Here's a little exercise to practice your eighth notes. Most of the time, the pieces in this book won't indicate how to play the eighth notes in melodies since there are several good approaches. Choose the technique that works best for you and try to keep it consistent.

24

Count: 1 2 3 4 1 & 2 & 3 & 4 & 1 & 2 & 3 & 4 & 1 & 2 3 4

LESSON 9: DOTTED QUARTER NOTES

VIDEO In Dotted Half Notes on page 34, you learned that a dot placed after a note head increases the duration by half of the original note value. A quarter note equals one beat. Half of that value is half a beat (equal to an eighth note), so a *dotted quarter note* equals one and one half beats (1½ beats). Dotted quarter notes very often are paired with an eighth note or eighth rest, either before or after the dotted quarter. This creates a grouping of notes that adds up to two beats.

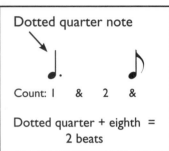

Dotted quarter note

Count: 1 & 2 &

Dotted quarter + eighth = 2 beats

Here is the familiar Beethoven melody "Ode to Joy." Look at each line before you start, and look for the dotted quarter and eighth-note rhythms. Each line creates a four-measure *phrase*, which is like a musical sentence. (For more on phrasing, see page 92.) Four-measure (as well as two-measure and eight-measure) phrases are very common and can help you identify patterns in the music. This melody is easier to learn if you practice the C Major scale (page 35) before you start. All of the notes in this piece are in the C Major scale.

VIDEO

ODE TO JOY
Theme to the Ninth Symphony (Opus 125)

Ludwig van Beethoven
(1770–1827)

VIDEO EXAMPLE ACCIDENTALS DO HAPPEN

Once you have become familiar with reading the natural notes, adding the accidentals (sharps and flats, see page 12) is simple. Here's a quick review:

Symbol	Name	Description
♯	Sharp	Raises a natural note by one half step (one fret).
♭	Flat	Lowers a natural note by one half step (one fret).
♮	Natural	Cancels a sharp or flat—play the natural note.

In written music, a sharp, flat, or natural will appear just to the left of the note it affects. When you say the note name out loud, say the letter first.

Say: "A-sharp   G-flat   A-natural"

ACCIDENTALS LAST FOR THE REST OF THE MEASURE
When a sharp or flat appears on a note, that note remains affected by the sharp or flat until the end of the measure. In other words, a sharp or flat can be canceled only by a natural or a bar line.

Here's a tune that will give you a chance to practice reading accidentals. You may need a little help finding the new notes at first so the TAB is also shown.

VIDEO EXAMPLE *RAISED BY GYPSIES*

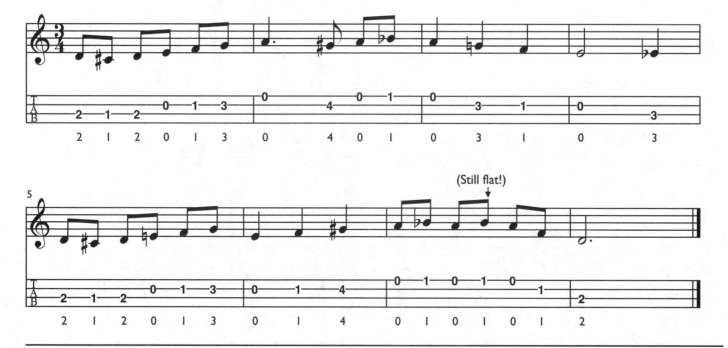

(Still flat!)

Most pieces of music have a *key* (see page 18). The key is named after the *tonal center* or *tonic* note. The tonic note is the first note of the scale for the key and the note that gives the strongest feeling of resolution or completion. Every major scale has its own unique set of notes, some of which may be sharp or flat. The *key signature* allows us to easily show which sharps or flats are in the key without cluttering the piece with accidentals.

A key signature appears just after the clef sign at the beginning of each line of music. It is a set of sharps or flats (never both). You will learn more in Chapter 4 about where key signatures come from and which keys they represent. If you see no key signature, it just means that the notes of the piece will all be natural notes, as in the key of C Major.

Reading a key signature is very simple. Look just to the right of the clef sign. Any sharps or flats that appear will affect that pitch throughout the entire piece of music. For instance, the key signature in the example to the right has an F♯ (F-sharp) and a C♯ (C-sharp). This means that *all* of the F notes and *all* of the C notes will be sharped unless marked with other accidentals.

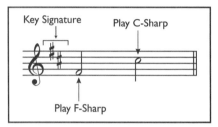

IMPORTANT NOTE
Accidentals in key signatures affect the notes in every octave, not just the line or space on which the accidental appears.

Try reading through the classic cowboy song "Red River Valley," below. The key signature contains one flat, B♭ (B-flat), which is the signature of F Major. The notes affected by the key signature have been circled to remind you that they are flatted, but this is just to help you out this one time! TAB is also included.

RED RIVER VALLEY

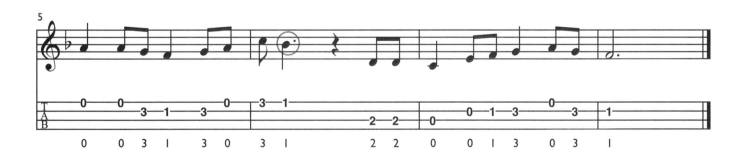

VIDEO EXAMPLE A *tie* combines two note values (on the same pitch) so that they are expressed as one note lasting for the combined duration of the two values. For example, in the example to the right, the third note is tied to the fourth note. You would play the third note, but not the fourth note, since it is *tied to* (and therefore part of) the third note. Hold the third note through its own value *and* the value of the note it's tied to.

Tie

One way to remember how to handle ties is "play the first note and hold through the second note." Ties can bind together two note values within a measure, or they can cross the bar line so that a note that begins in one measure can last into the next measure.

Below is an exercise to work on reading ties and a new key signature. "King on the Beach" is in D Major, which contains F♯ and C♯. This time, you're on your own to make sure to find all the notes affected by the key signature. The TAB will help you catch any mistakes.

VIDEO EXAMPLE *KING ON THE BEACH*

MORE ABOUT TIES

Ties connect notes of the same pitch. If you see an arc shape that looks like a tie but the connected notes are different, it's called a *slur*. Slurs do not change the rhythm, they affect the way you articulate the notes on the instrument. You'll learn about slurs on the ukulele later. An arc shape above the staff is a *phrase mark* (page 92).

Ties are sometimes used in situations where a simpler note value might make the rhythm harder to read. For example, a dotted quarter (1½ beats) might be followed by a note that lasts for one beat. It would seem sensible to write a quarter note for the second note, but it is more clear to write the second note as two eighths tied together (see right). This preserves the convention of each dotted quarter pairing with an eighth, making it easier to quickly understand the rhythm.

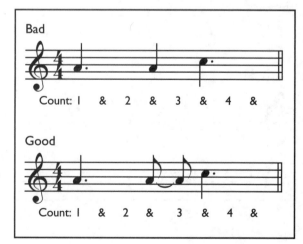

LESSON 13: NAVIGATING A MUSICAL MAP

The following short piece contains some devices that allow a longer musical idea to fit into a shorter space on the page. The repeat sign at the end of the fourth bar tells you to repeat from the beginning. The *first ending* (measures 3 and 4) indicates the music you should play on the first time through. The *second ending* indicates that on the second time through, you should play the second ending instead of the first ending.

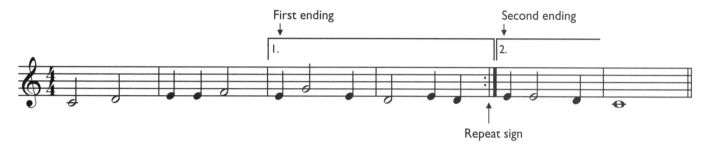

The markings above tell you to follow these steps:
1. Play measures 1 through 4 as normal.
2. Repeat from the beginning, playing measures 1 and 2.
3. At measure 3, skip over both measures 3 and 4 (the first ending), and, instead, play the second ending (the last two measures of the tune).

Following are a few other markings you might see as you become more advanced. They are provided as a reference. Like many musical markings, they originate in Italian terms.

D.C.	D.C. stands for *Da Capo*, Italian for "from the head." It tells you to repeat the whole piece of music from the beginning.
D.S. 𝄋	D.S. stands for *Dal Segno* (pronounced "sane-yo"), meaning "from the sign." D.S. tells you to look for the special sign (shown at left) earlier in the music and repeat the music from that point.
al Fine	*Fine* (pronounced "fee-nay") means "the end." *Al Fine* can be added to *D.C.* or *D.S.* Repeat the piece as indicated by *D.C.* or *D.S.*, but end your second pass through the piece at the end of the measure marked "*Fine.*"
al Coda ⨁	A *coda* (meaning "tail") is new music added to the end of a piece. *Al Coda* can be added to *D.C.* or *D.S.* Repeat the piece as indicated by *D.C.* or *D.S.* up until you see the first coda symbol (shown at left). At this point, jump to a later point in the music marked with the second coda symbol and continue from there.

The markings above all require you to jump from one section of the written music to another without interrupting the flow of the music. Always check out a piece of music before you start playing it, looking for repeats, endings, and other similar directions. You may need to plan out where the "jumps" are, and even highlight them on the music so you know where to go ahead of time.

CHAPTER 4

Theory Without Fear, or a Little Knowledge Can Get You Jamming

THEORY IS GIVING NAMES TO SOUNDS

This chapter will give you some basic theory tools to accelerate your learning, jamming, and improvising. In music, *theory* is the collection of terms and concepts used to describe musical sounds and how they interact. Learning theory will not ruin the spontaneity and creativity of your playing—theory doesn't tell you how to play, it just tells you how to describe it.

LESSON 1: THE MAJOR SCALE IS YOUR MEASURING STICK

TWO FOUNDATIONS: THE CHROMATIC SCALE AND THE MAJOR SCALE

The foundations of music theory in the Western, or European, tradition are the chromatic scale and major scale. The chromatic scale, or music alphabet (see page 12), gives us the 12 tones in each octave on our instrument. If you're still shaky on the chromatic scale, go back and learn it by heart before proceeding.

The major scale gives us a very common set of notes and relationships we can use to make music. We also use the major scale as a "standard of measurement" to compare all the other scales to, much like we would compare a prize-winning giant cucumber to a ruler to see how long it was. Below is the C Major scale you learned on page 35. The notes can be numbered 1–7, with the 8th note being the same as note number 1 in the next octave. These numbers are called *scale degrees*.

25

Note:	C	D	E	F	G	A	B	C
Scale Degree:	1	2	3	4	5	6	7	8(1)

```
T|------------------------------------0---2---3--
A|------------------0---1---3--------------------
B|----0---2----------------------------------
     0   2   0   1   3   0   2   3
```

VIDEO EXAMPLE   THE SECRET FORMULA

The C Major scale is made by playing the natural notes C–D–E–F–G–A–B–C. You know from the music alphabet that there is a half step between B and C, and also between E and F. All of the other letters are a whole step apart. In terms of scale degrees, the half steps are between notes 3 and 4, and between notes 7 and 8 (which could also be called note 1). This gives us the series of whole steps and half steps that make every major scale. To the right is the C Major scale with the intervals and scale degrees shown.

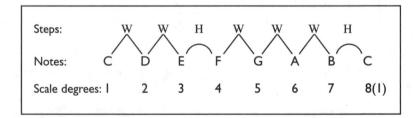

Steps:	W	W	H	W	W	W	H
Notes:	C	D	E	F	G	A	B	C
Scale degrees:	1	2	3	4	5	6	7	8(1)

W = Whole step
H = Half step

With careful use of the formula, you can *spell* (apply the formula of whole steps and half steps) the major scale starting on any note. Just start with the key note (1st scale degree) and then follow the formula, using each letter only once. The D Major scale is shown below. Notice that to make E to F a whole step, as the formula requires, we must raise the F a half step to F♯. Try spelling the A and B♭ Major scales (the correct answers are underneath the Hot Tips box below).

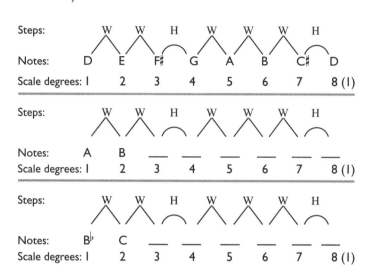

Answers:

Notes:	B♭	C	D	E♭	F	G	A	B♭
Scale degrees:	1	2	3	4	5	6	7	8 (1)

Notes:	A	B	C♯	D	E	F♯	G♯	A
Scale degrees:	1	2	3	4	5	6	7	8 (1)

Try playing the A Major scale by going up the 1st string. Playing the scale on a single string makes it easy to see the whole steps and half steps. When you get comfortable with it, try going backwards! You will learn other fingerings for major scales in different keys later in this book series.

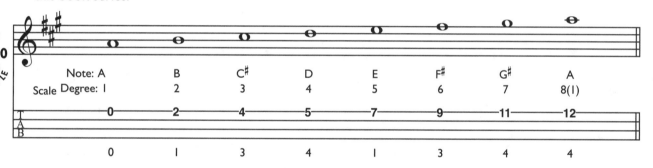

LESSON 2: THE CIRCLE OF 5THS

The *circle of 5ths* is like the "secret agent decoder ring" of music theory. (And you don't have to send in any cereal box tops to get it!) A *5th* is the distance between the 1st and 5th degrees of a scale. To make a circle of 5ths, just take the keys and arrange them in a circle so that the next keynote (going clockwise) is the 5th degree of the last scale. For example, the 5th degree of a D Major scale is A, so the next key in the circle is A.

The circle of 5ths makes it easy to learn the key signature for each key. The "sharp keys" (clockwise on the circle) add one sharp for each new key. The new sharp is always the 7th scale degree of that key. The "flat keys" (counterclockwise) add one new flat for each key. That new flat is always the 4th scale degree of the key.

Notice that the keys of G♭ and F♯ are in the same position in the circle. The two scales are played on exactly the same strings and frets and sound exactly the same. Remember, when two notes have the same sound but different names, they are *enharmonic equivalents*.

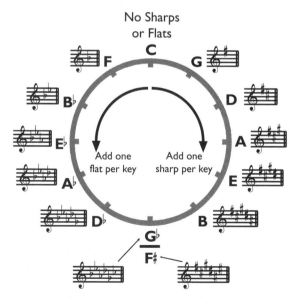

LESSON 3: INTERVALS ARE YOUR BUILDING BLOCKS

Along with the music alphabet and the major scale, *intervals* are a fundamental element of music theory. An interval is the distance between two notes, measured in steps. You've already worked with a couple of intervals: the half step (known in interval lingo as a *minor 2nd*) and the whole step (*major 2nd*).

VIDEO EXAMPLE HOW INTERVALS ARE NAMED

Interval names include a number (like 2nd or 3rd) and a word that describes the interval's *quality* (major, minor, augmented, diminished, or perfect). The number describes how many steps, or letters in the music alphabet, are spanned by the interval. The quality helps describe the interval more precisely. The distance in an interval is always calculated from the lower of the two pitches to the higher.

THE INTERVALS IN ONE OCTAVE AND HOW TO PLAY THEM

Because of its unique reentrant tuning, there are many ways to play the various intervals on the ukulele. You will encounter many of them as your learning progresses. The important thing right now is that you become familiar with the naming system for intervals and their sounds. A simple way to do this is to use the 4th string (G) as a constant root note and making the intervals above G on the 2nd and 1st strings. Here are all the intervals in one octave using G as the lowest note (or root). The note names are shown above the music. You can play the intervals *harmonically* (together, as shown) or *melodically* (one note after the other). After you have tried them out, you will learn about the different types.

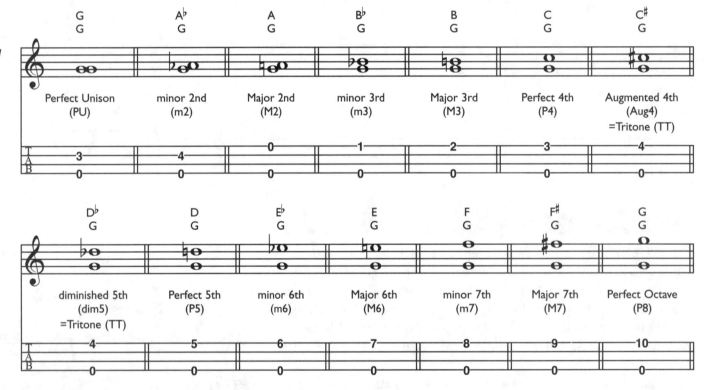

THEORY TIP

The intervals shown above are arranged from the smallest to the largest, with the augmented 4th and diminished 5th producing the enharmonic names of the same note (C♯ and D♭). It's a great idea to memorize the names of the intervals in ascending order as well as their half steps. The chart on the next page shows the intervals and half steps.

The chart to the right shows the intervals and their abbreviations from smallest to largest by half steps.

PERFECT INTERVALS

There are only four intervals in an octave that are described as *perfect*. They are the unison, the 4th, the 5th, and the octave (or PU, P4, P5, and P8). These intervals do not come in major and minor versions (see below). When the two notes of a perfect interval are played together on a well tuned instrument, they resonate with great clarity, like a camera lens that is in perfect focus.

MAJOR AND MINOR INTERVALS

The following intervals come in major or minor versions: 2nds, 3rds, 6ths, and 7ths. In the case of any one of these intervals, the *major* interval is larger, or farther apart, by one half step. The *minor* interval is smaller, or closer together, by one half step. The abbreviations for major intervals use an uppercase "M," while the minor intervals use a lowercase "m." The major and perfect intervals correspond to the steps in the major scale (see below).

Interval	Abbreviation	Half Steps
Perfect Unison	PU	0
minor 2nd	m2	1
Major 2nd	M2	2
minor 3rd	m3	3
Major 3rd	M3	4
Perfect 4th	P4	5
Augmented 4th (or Tritone)	Aug4 or TT	6
Diminished 5th (or Tritone)	dim5 or TT	6
Perfect 5th	P5	7
minor 6th	m6	8
Major 6th	M6	9
minor 7th	m7	10
Major 7th	M7	11
Perfect Octave	P8	12

AUGMENTED AND DIMINISHED INTERVALS

All types of intervals can be augmented or diminished. To augment means to add to or make bigger. An *augmented* interval is one half step larger than a major or perfect interval. To diminish means to make smaller. A *diminished* interval is one half step smaller than a minor or perfect interval.

THE TRITONE (AUGMENTED 4TH/DIMINISHED 5TH)

Between the perfect 4th and perfect 5th is an interval called a *tritone* (abbreviated TT). "Tone" is another word for whole step, so, a tritone equals three whole steps (equivalent to six half steps). In the interval naming system, a tritone is either an augmented 4th (one half step larger than a perfect 4th) or a diminished 5th (one half step smaller than a perfect 5th). Both the augmented 4th and the diminished 5th refer to the same distance of six half steps.

INTERVALS OF THE MAJOR SCALE

You can use the major scale as a reference for your intervals. To make a major scale, use only the perfect and major intervals. You can then find the minor intervals by lowering any major interval by one half step. Below are the intervals of the G Major scale. The upper notes show the scale, while the lower note remains G throughout to show the interval distances from the tonic.

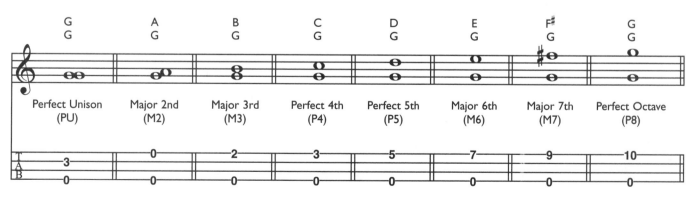

VIDEO EXAMPLE Remember, a chord is any three or more notes played together. The subject of chords and how they behave is called *harmony*. The most basic kind of chord is called a *triad*. A triad is a three-note chord, generally made by stacking one interval of a 3rd on top of another. You have already learned several major and minor chords, and some 6th and 7th chords. The major and minor chords are triads (sometimes with a note repeated if you are strumming all four strings). The 6th and 7th chords have four notes.

Below is a C Major scale that has been *harmonized*. This means that 3rds have been stacked above each note of the scale to form triads. The harmony notes are all within the scale—no sharps or flats have been added or changed. This is called *diatonic harmony,* or harmony within the key. TAB has been included so it will be easy for you to hear what the harmonized scale sounds like. You can also play the chords using any other familiar fingerings. You will find three types of triads: major, minor, and diminished, which are all discussed below.

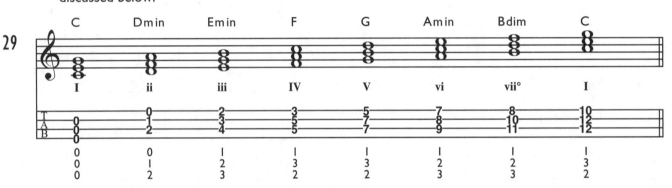

Notice that the chords have been designated with Roman numerals. This allows for a distinction between scale degrees and chord numbers. The Roman numerals also show the quality of the chord (uppercase for major chords, and lowercase for minor and diminished chords). Diminished chords are also labeled with a small superscript circle (as in B°).

Roman Numeral Review

I or i	1	V or v	5
II or ii	2	VI or vi	6
III or iii	3	VII or vii	7
IV or iv	4		

THREE KINDS OF TRIADS
The three types of triads that result from harmonizing the major scale are all made with different combinations of major and minor 3rds.

- A *major triad* is a major 3rd with a minor 3rd on top. Its structure is root–3rd–5th.

- A *minor triad* is a minor 3rd with a major 3rd on top. Its structure is root–♭3rd–5th.

- A *diminished triad* is a minor 3rd with another minor 3rd on top. Its structure is root–♭3rd–♭5th.

For comparison, this example shows the three types of triads, all built on a C root.

TRIAD STRUCTURE
The bottom note of the triad is the *root*. The root is always the note the chord is named for. The middle note, which is a 3rd above the root, is called the *3rd*. The top note, which is a 3rd above the 3rd and a 5th above the root, is called the *5th*.

5th
3rd
Root

THREE PRIMARY CHORDS

The *primary chords* in every major key are the I, IV, and V (one, four, and five) chords.

Here is a C Major scale with the roots of the I, IV, and V chords circled.

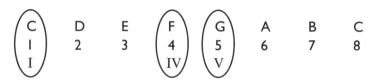

Below is a chord progression using I, IV, and V. The key of C Major is indicated. Also try it in D and G. Use any chord fingerings or strum patterns you like.

Key of C Major

Key of D Major
Fill in the blanks. The answers are at the bottom of the page.

Key of G Major
Fill in the blanks. The answers are at the bottom of the page.

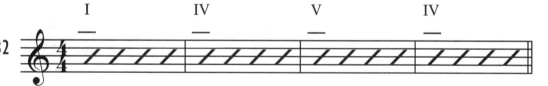

THE TRIUMPHANT RETURN OF THE CIRCLE OF 5THS

The circle of 5ths can be used to show basic harmonic movement. Instead of keys, these are major chords. Box or circle any three adjacent chords. The one in the middle is I. The one going clockwise is V. The one going counterclockwise is IV.

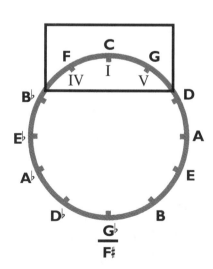

Answers:

Key of D: D G A   Key of G: G C D
           I IV V   I IV V

CHAPTER 5

Old-Time Ukulele and Backing Up Fiddle Tunes

Old-time music is an American traditional style based on fiddle tunes and songs that were played for dances and parties in the late 1800s and early 1900s. The roots of the music are in tunes that have been played for hundreds of years in Europe and the British Isles, mixed with influences from Africa, Native Americans, and immigrant cultures. Old-time music is one of the roots of more recent styles like bluegrass and Americana.

Old-time music is a community music and lots of fun to play along with. Sometimes a picking session is just a few people, but some jams can get very large with many fiddles, banjos, and guitars. The portability and unique voice of the uke have made it an adopted member of the old-time family. The banjo uke (see page 7) is a particular favorite in old-time jams because it is louder and more percussive than wooden ukes, but you can play with any type of uke.

The role of the uke in an old-time jam is generally as part of the rhythm section (along with guitars and upright basses). Since the uke is high pitched and has little sustain, it projects best when strumming chords in a steady rhythm. The constant, repetitive groove made by the rhythm section provides a foundation for the fiddles, banjos, and mandolins to play syncopated melodies against.

THE COMMON FIDDLE KEYS

The fiddle is a central instrument in old-time music. The keys of C, G, D, and A allow the fiddle to make use of its open strings for extra harmony notes, and so these keys have become the most common keys for tunes. This chapter will focus on playing in D, G, and A, since you've already played several songs in C. It's a good idea to memorize the primary chords (I, IV, and V) for these common keys. That way, when someone tells you the key for a tune, you'll have at least an idea of what some of the chords might be. The chart to the right shows what you need to know.

KEY	I	IV	V
C	C	F	G or G7
G	G	C	D or D7
D	D	G	A or A7
A	A	D	E or E7

Jeff Claus—*of the Ithaca, New York band The Horse Flies*—*helped spark new interest in using the banjo uke to accompany old-time music starting in the mid-1980s. The Horse Flies play traditional acoustic fiddle tunes with drive and momentum, but they are also known for using echo and wah effects to create minimalist soundscapes reminiscent of composer Steve Reich, and for their influences of punk, indie, and new wave.*

You can use your index finger to strum old-time music. Let your strumming motion come from a loose, relaxed wrist and fingers. Many uke players who play old-time music like to use a pick instead. A long high-energy jam can really wear down your fingernail if you're not careful. See page 28 for more on picks. Here are a couple of strums that work well for old-time uke. The first one ought to be pretty familiar by now! Try each one many times over using different chords.

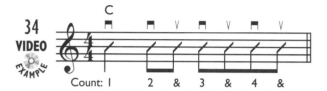

Below are the chords to a classic old-time and bluegrass song also known as "Nine Pound Hammer" or "Roll On, Buddy." Try it with the second strum shown above, or mix up the strum patterns. Stay loose, because these tunes can get pretty fast in jam situations! This tune is in the key of G. The chords are G (I), C (IV), and D (V).

THIS HAMMER'S TOO HEAVY

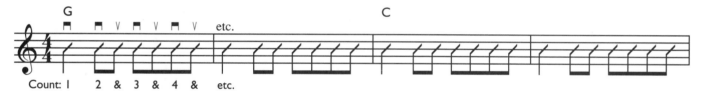

C TUNING OR D TUNING?

You can ignore this box and lead a happy uke life, but if you're curious about tunings, read on. This book is written for ukuleles tuned G–C–E–A, also known as C or C6 tuning. Some players like to tune a whole step higher to A–D–F♯–B. This is known as D or D6 tuning. Here's where it helps to know the I, IV, and V chords in common keys. In D tuning, just transpose the chord shapes for each key down a whole step from what you normally use in C tuning.

For example, if you were playing in the key of D in standard C tuning, your chord shapes would be D (I), G (IV), and A (V). If you were playing in the key of D in D tuning, your chord shapes would be fingered like C, F, and G in C tuning. The D tuning is a whole step higher, so the corresponding chord shapes are a whole step lower.

You can simulate this on a standard tuned uke by placing a capo (a device that clamps the strings down to a fret) at the 2nd fret. Some players also like the D tuning because it puts more tension on the strings, giving the uke an even brighter, snappier tone when strummed.

One way to inject more propulsion into the old-time groove is to accent the backbeat. An *accent* (>) is a musical symbol that tells you to play a note or chord louder than the surrounding notes. Many grooves in blues, jazz, rock, bluegrass, and old-time are based on a four-beat rhythm pattern: bass note or kick drum on beats 1 and 3, and a high-pitched sound like a snare drum or guitar chord on 2 and 4. Beats 2 and 4 in this rhythm are called the *backbeat*. This rhythm has its roots in the basic foot-stomp and handclap rhythm that accompanied spirituals and work songs sung by Africans in America during the era of slavery. The backbeat rhythm became the heartbeat of many styles of music.

Try the following strum using a medium volume for most of the strokes and a louder strum on beats 2 and 4. You can achieve this with a stronger snap of the wrist, or by flicking your finger a little more forcefully. If you're using a pick, hold the pick a little tighter on the accent beats and you'll hear them pop out.

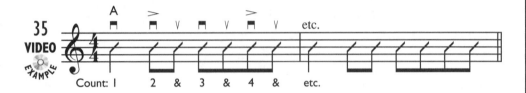

In the key of A, I is an A chord, IV is D, and V is E or E7. Finger E using three or four fingers, or by barring one finger. You may find E7 easier at first.

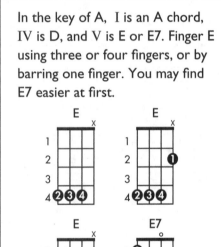

Here are the chords to "Sally Ann" in the key of A, using the accented backbeat strum. "Sally Ann" has two sections, the A part and the B part. Each part is repeated, and the whole tune can be played many times. Note the *right-facing repeat* at the start of the B part; it tells you that the repeat at the end of the B part (*left-facing*) begins here.

VIDEO EXAMPLE *SALLY ANN*

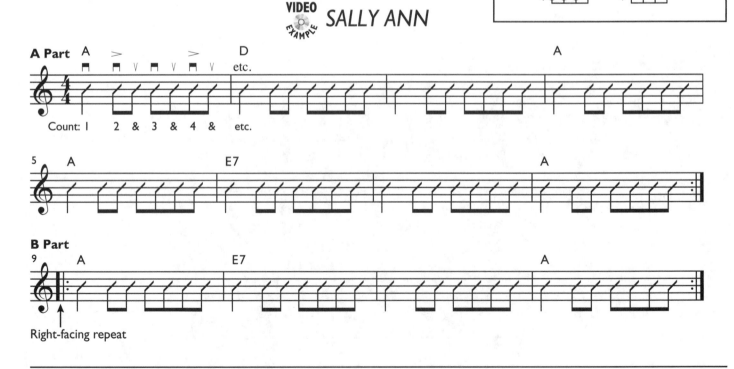

Right-facing repeat

Form is the internal structure that repeats (or cycles through a series of sections) to make up a piece of music. One of the most common forms in old-time music is the *two-part fiddle tune*. This form is known in classical theory as a *binary form*. The two main sections of the tune are labeled the A part and the B part. Each part is repeated before moving on. The basic form of the tune can be described as "A A B B." This form is then repeated over and over for as long as the group wants to jam on it.

One of the oldest and most popular tunes in the repertoire is "Soldier's Joy" in the key of D. The I, IV, and V chords are D, G, and A respectively. Don't forget to repeat both the A part and the B part. The melody is a little tricky to play on the uke, but a simplified version is shown with TAB if you want to try it (pay close attention to the fingering shown below the TAB!). On the video, you'll hear the melody played by the fiddle, as well as a bass line to give you the feel of a real jam. Use any of the patterns from this chapter to strum.

VIDEO EXAMPLE · SOLDIER'S JOY

CHAPTER 6

Old School: The Swingin' Ukulele

The first big wave of international popularity for the ukulele came in the early decades of the 1900s. During this same period, various streams of popular music—including parlor songs of the 1800s, ragtime, marching band music, and blues—were combining and evolving into jazz. The jazz and swing band music heard on the radio and in dance halls was sophisticated and virtuosic, requiring experienced musicians and a lot of practice. When the ukulele came along, it offered the average person an accessible way to capture some of the energy and rhythm of a swing band. The uke was relatively inexpensive and you could carry it to the college pep rally in the pocket of your oversize fur coat (an essential fashion item of the time).

TIN PAN ALLEY AND HAPA HAOLE

The fad of the ukulele and Hawaiian music (or semi-Hawaiian music) took over the 1920s, and many modern uke enthusiasts still play the songs and styles that evolved during this era. A major source of material in this period were the writers and publishers of sheet music for popular songs. This industry was based in New York City and is referred to as "Tin Pan Alley." The Tin Pan Alley writers worked night and day to create new songs that could be sold to a public that was hungry to join whatever fad was hot at the moment. They created hundreds of songs that combined Hawaiian words, fake Hawaiian-sounding language, and humorous or romantic themes in English set to the popular swing rhythms of the day. These mixed-language songs became known as *hapa haole* songs, where *hapa* (pronounced HAH-pah) means half, and *haole* (pronounced HOW-leh) means non-native or Caucasian.

LESSON 1: HOW TO SWING

VIDEO EXAMPLE

The basis of swing and jazz music is a way of counting and feeling the underlying beat of the music. You have already played music with eighth notes, so you know that eighth notes divide the beat into two equal pieces. This type of eighth notes is called *straight eighths*.

There is another way to count eighth notes called *swing eighths*. In swing eighths, the onbeat is given longer emphasis while the offbeat ("&") is made shorter. In straight eighths the beat is divided into two equal pieces. In the swing feel, the pulse of the beat is divided into three pieces, or eighth-note triplets. To count triplets, try saying this aloud to a steady beat: "Tri-pul-let, tri-pul-let."

In swing eighths, the first two notes of the triplet are tied together, so that you don't hear an individual note on the second eighth. In the swing feel, this rhythm happens so much that it becomes unwieldy to write and count full triplets all the time. Instead, the swing-eighths rhythm is counted as if it were eighth notes with an onbeat that is twice as long as the offbeat.

Straight Eighths

Count: 1 & 2 & 3 & 4 &

Triplets

Tri - pul - let   Tri - pul - let   Tri - pul - let   Tri - pul - let

The Swing-Eighths Feel

1 & 2 & 3 & 4 &

Swing eighths are designated at the beginning of a piece of music in one of two ways (see right). If you see either designation, it means all eighth notes in the piece are to be "swung."

Grab a C chord on your ukulele and try strumming and counting some swing eighths. This next example introduces a new symbol called the *simile mark*. It looks like a slash with a dot on either side. The simile mark tells you to duplicate whatever you were doing in the previous measure. In the following examples, it tells you to continue the same strumming pattern.

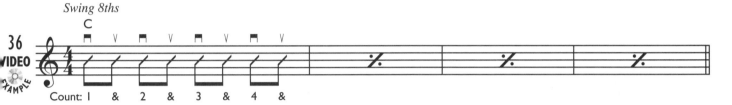

Now try your trusty quarter-and-two-eighths strum using the swing-eighths feel. This makes a great strum for swing tunes. Try it with different chords or make up some progressions.

VIDEO I SEE YOU'VE GONE STACCATO

Here's a nifty way to put a little jump in your swing strum. You have already learned a bit about legato and staccato (page 34). Remember, legato means the notes are held for their full duration, which is the normal, or "default," way that we play notes and chords. Staccato means the sustain of the note or chord is cut off early, resulting in a "clipped" sound for that beat. You can play a staccato chord by relaxing the pressure of the fretting fingers just after you strum the chord. Don't take them all the way off the strings. Technically, this is not full staccato, because the open strings in the chord will still be ringing, but it is enough to give a nice texture to the groove.

Try the following strum on a G chord with staccato chords on beats 1, 2, and 3. Staccato is indicated with a dot above or below the note head, opposite the stem. Use the squeezing and relaxing pressure of your left-hand fingers to create the staccato. You can also throw in staccato notes to other strum patterns.

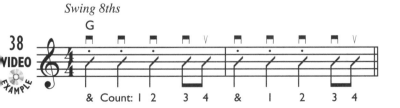

JAZZY PROGRESSIONS NEED JAZZY CHORDS

One of the most recognizable characteristics of jazz and swing is the use of chords that move beyond the three notes of the triad. As soon as a fourth note is added to a chord, it becomes more colorful and complex.

6TH CHORDS

As you have learned, a major triad consists of a root, 3rd, and 5th, corresponding to the first, third, and fifth notes of a major scale. If you add the sixth note of the major scale to the triad, you get a *major 6th chord*. An example (shown on the right) is the C6 chord, which contains the notes C, E, G, and A (root, 3rd, 5th, and 6th).

Below are fingerings for 6th chords based on the major chords you have learned. As you learn each one, try alternating the 6th chord with the corresponding major chord. This will help you see the similarity and hear the difference between them.

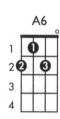

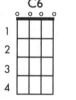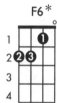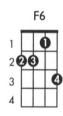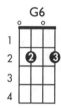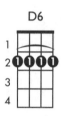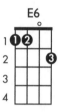

Try the progression below. It may look difficult to switch chords every two beats, but if you look carefully you will notice that you only have to move one or two fingers in each bar to make the change. It's very common to use 6th chords alternating with major or 7th chords to give melodic motion within one basic chord. Remember that you can lift on the last upstroke of the bar in order to move to the next chord in time.

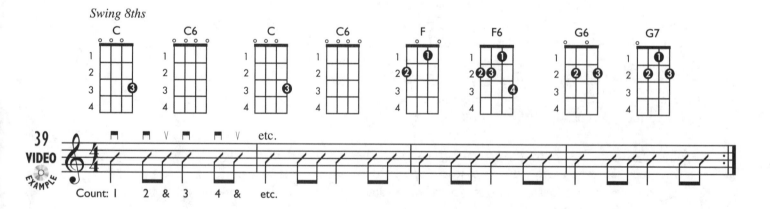

Swing 8ths

> * This F6 should remind you of Dmin, because it has the same notes! A full F6 chord contains F, A, C, and D. This fingering only contains F, A, and D, which also make up a Dmin chord. This fingering for F6 is shown here because it is easy to get to from the familiar two-finger F chord. On the uke, it is not uncommon to have chord voicings that leave out a note or two from the full versions of the chords. The next F6 contains all of the notes in the chord.

The next progression gives you a chance to try out D6, A6, and E6 from the previous page. If D6 gives you trouble as a one-finger barre chord (see page 66 for tips), you can try fingering the normal three-finger D chord you've been using and add the 4th finger on the 2nd fret of the 1st string to make it D6. This progression uses the staccato strum you learned in the previous lesson. It works well here because these chords have few open strings, making it easier to hear the staccato notes cut off as you relax the pressure of your fingers.

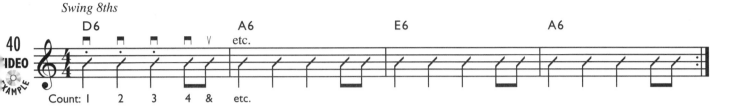

DOMINANT 7TH CHORDS

A *7th chord* is made by stacking another 3rd on top of a triad (root–3rd–5th–7th). There are several types of 7th chords. The type you are going to learn first is called a *dominant 7th chord*. The dominant 7th chord is a major triad with a minor 7th ($\flat$7) added. The chord symbol for a dominant 7th chord consists of a root note followed by the number 7 (as in G7). For example, the G7 chord contains the notes G–B–D–F (root–3rd–5th–$\flat$7th).

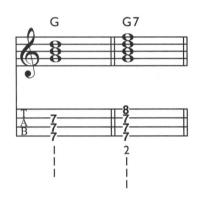

You have learned many of these dominant 7th chords already, but here they are for review. A few have multiple fingering/voicing options. You'll be using some of these dominant 7ths in the next lesson, so make sure you can do at least one fingering for each.

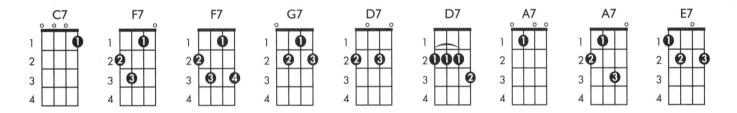

"DOMINANT" IS ANOTHER WORD FOR THE V CHORD

The name *dominant* refers to the 5th note (or V chord) of a major scale. The dominant 7th chord is the type of 7th chord that occurs on the V chord in a major key. For example, the G7 chord discussed above is the V chord of the key of C Major, and all of its notes are found in the C Major scale.

Dominant 7th chords can be used as the V chord of a major key, but they can also be used to add additional color to major triads. Sometimes it sounds great, other times it adds too much color to the chord. The best approach is to try it and see if you like it. Here's a tip if you're overwhelmed by learning lots of chords at once: In any situation that calls for a 6th chord or dominant 7th chord, you can play the plain major chord instead. The major triad is part of each of these chords, so all you would be doing is leaving a note out. No problem!

VIDEO EXAMPLE The roots of jazz are in *ragtime*, a popular form of music in the late 1800s and early 1900s. Ragtime was known for its syncopated rhythms, catchy tunes, and virtuosic performers. One of the most common progressions to come out of ragtime is the *circle of 5ths progression*. This progression creates an unusual sound because it does not follow all of the diatonic chord qualities of the major scale.

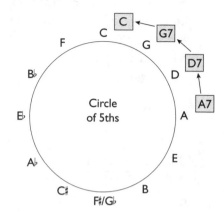

Imagine that the circle of 5ths shown on the right represents major chords. If you follow the circle counterclockwise, each chord is the V chord of the next chord in the circle. When we use V chords that belong to chords other than the I chord of the key, they are called *secondary dominants*.

A circle of 5ths progression usually follows four chords around the circle (going counterclockwise), with the last chord being the I chord of the key. The other three chords can be played as dominant 7ths to increase the sense of each chord being a V chord to the next; for example, the progression shown in the highlighted chords in the illustration above goes A7–D7–G7–C. This is a circle of 5ths progression in C Major.

You can play circle of 5ths progressions by following any set of four adjacent chords counterclockwise around the circle. Try it with major chords and with dominant 7ths. To get you started, here's a progression in C that begins on C (the I chord), then jumps to A7 and follows the circle of 5ths counterclockwise back to C. There are probably thousands of songs that include this progression or something like it!

41 VIDEO EXAMPLE

PHOTO BY WILLIAM P. GOTTLIEB

Cliff Edwards (1895–1971), known by his nickname "Ukulele Ike," was a prolific recording artist and performer during the uke heyday of the '20s and '30s. The massive popularity of his records, including a #1 hit recording of "Singin' in the Rain," helped inspire the sale of vast numbers of ukuleles and Tin Pan Alley songs in sheet music. Edwards appeared in movies as an actor/singer and as a voice actor for animated films. His most known role was as the voice of Jiminy Cricket in the 1940 Disney movie Pinnochio.

Here, we move the same progression to the key of F. Can you find the chords on the circle of 5ths?

The next example moves the progression to the key of G, then follows with a typical ragtime treatment. The strums are shown to give you some rhythm ideas. The third line has a new *syncopated* rhythm like the horn section might play in a big band. In syncopated rhythms, emphasis is placed on the offbeats rather than the onbeats (for more on syncopation, see page 62).

VIDEO EXAMPLE HOW WILL I EVER LEARN TO CHARLESTON IF I CAN'T EVEN TIE MY OWN SHOES?

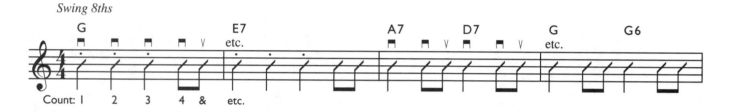

LESSON 4: THE TRIPLE STRUM

The ukulele is one of the easiest instruments to play for simple song accompaniment. It is also capable of fun and somewhat acrobatic special effects, especially in the form of unique strums. So far, your strums have involved just two strokes: the downstroke and upstroke. The *triple strum* (also called a *triple stroke* or just a *triple*) adds an extra stroke to the mix, creating a three-stroke pattern that can be placed in the rhythm in various ways.

The triple strum works best using a combination of thumb and fingers. You can simulate the motion with a pick, but you may have a hard time getting as much speed as you can with the thumb and finger. There are several ways to execute a triple. Here, you will learn the "down-down-up" technique.

The triple strum is not synonymous with a rhythmic triplet. Though triple strums can be played in a triplet rhythm, they can also be adapted to a variety of other rhythms.

TRIPLE STRUM: DOWN-DOWN-UP

The following photos show the unused fingers curled up into the palm. This is just so you can see the motion of the active fingers better. In reality, you can either curl your unused fingers under or let them hang out extended. Stay relaxed and loose!

1. Downstroke with index finger (or with a combination of middle and ring fingers).
2. Downstroke with thumb.
3. Upstroke with index finger.

Below are several bars of the triple strum in $\frac{3}{4}$ time so you can practice giving each stroke equal time and emphasis. Try the triple strum on lots of different chords.

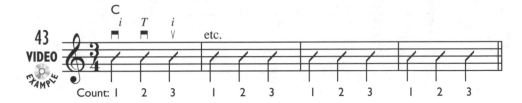

TWO TRIPLES AND A DOUBLE IN ONE BAR, OR, 3+3+2

While this may sound like a lovely evening out after a hard day at work, it's actually just a way to include triples into a measure of eighth notes.

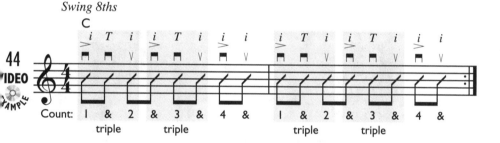

THE TRIPLE AS A TRIPLET

Here, the triple strum is used to play triplet eighth notes on the last beat of the measure. Remember, the eighth notes are swung, so the triplet feel is already present in the rhythm. All you have to do is insert the thumb downstroke between the normal downstroke and upstroke on the fourth beat.

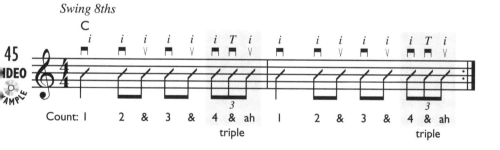

On the next page, you'll put these patterns into practice. You can also use them to strum through the progressions earlier in this chapter, or just sprinkle them into another pattern to spice things up.

The following exercise uses the 3+3+2 strum in the first four measures, then the triplet triple strum in the next three measures. The triple strums have been highlighted. This exercise also contains a four-finger version of F7 in measure four that you might not have tried yet. If you're having trouble getting the triple strums together, try strumming through this progression a few times with simple swing eighths using the regular down-up alternating motion. Practice the triple strum patterns separately and then try plugging them into the progression as they get easier.

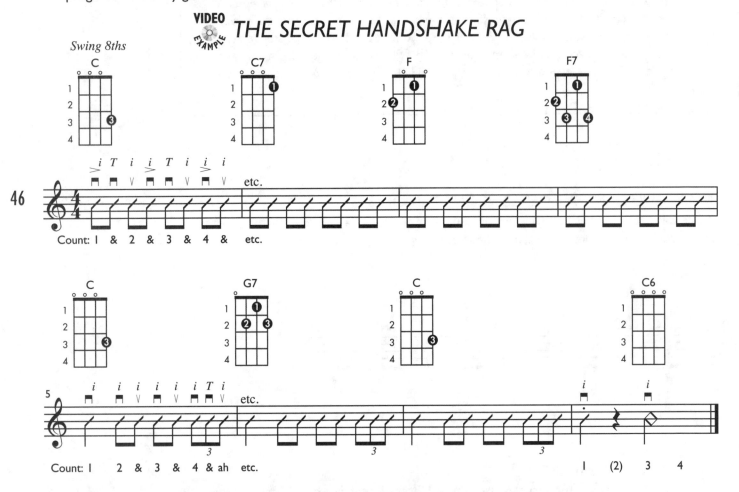

THE SECRET HANDSHAKE RAG

LESSON 5: THE TRIPLE BURST STRUM

You have learned how to incorporate the triple strum into regular eighth-note strumming. You can also learn to do triples very fast and use them as a flourish to accentuate a normal rhythm. These types of flourishes are sometimes called *bursts, rolls,* or *shakes* after both the sound and the quick movement of the hand.

VIDEO INTRODUCING THE SIXTEENTH-NOTE TRIPLET

The triple burst is shown as a *sixteenth-note triplet. Sixteenth notes* look like eighth notes, but with a double beam, or a double flag for single sixteenths. Normal sixteenth notes divide a quarter note into four pieces, counted "1-e-&-a."

Triplet sixteenths, like all triplets, allow you to fit three notes where there are normally two. Normal sixteenths are *two* equal notes in the space of an eighth note. Triplet sixteenths are *three* equal notes in the space of one eighth note. One common way to count two sets of sixteenth-note triplets (one full beat's worth) is "1-la-li-&-la-li." This can be a tongue twister if the tempos are fast, so an alternative is "1-a-la-&-a-la."

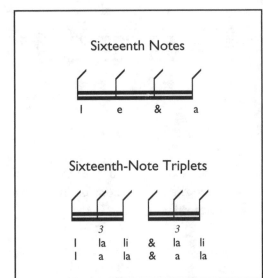

A *triple burst* is a sixteenth-note triplet followed by an accented downstroke. The triplet falls on the "&" of the beat before the accented downbeat. The end result should sound like a burst of four strums (kind of like a machine-gun burst), with the last strum falling on a strong downbeat. To get an idea of how it fits in the rhythm, try saying this out loud "gimme a BEAT!" In that phrase, "gimme a" is the triplet, and "BEAT!" is the accented downbeat.

Here is a triple burst consisting of a down-down-up (*i-T-i*) triple strum immediately followed by an accented downstroke of the *i* finger.

You can also do triple bursts using just downstrokes and upstrokes of the index finger or pick. The tricky thing is that the final accented beat will fall on an upstroke instead of a normal downstroke.

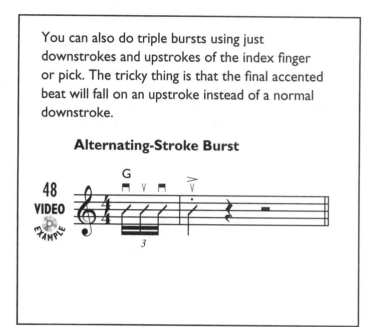

The example below contains a lot of information, but it's not too difficult if you think it through. The basic strum is a staccato quarter note followed by eighth notes. On the last eighth of the measure (the "&" of 4), do a triplet sixteenth-note burst into the accented first beat of the next bar. Don't forget to swing the eighths!

HITCH IN MY GIT-ALONG RAG

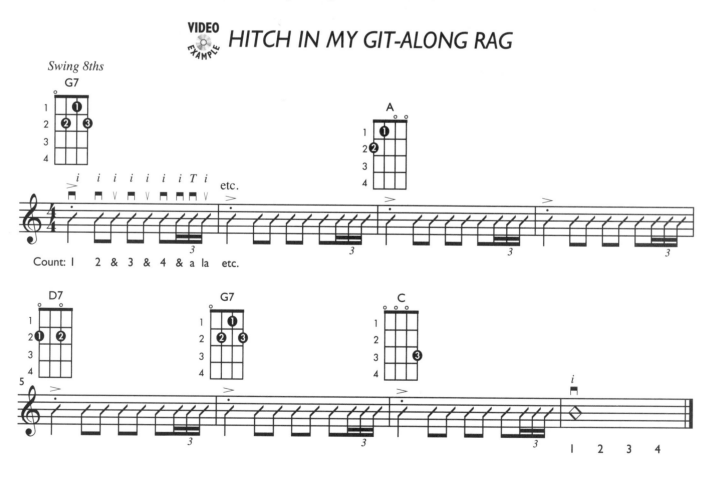

CHAPTER 7

Rocking Out the Uke

In recent years, the uke has come to be a symbol for musicians who are a little different, who don't travel the well-worn path. The uke has snuck into punk clubs, songwriter listening rooms, and major pop hits like "Hey, Soul Sister" by Train. Nowhere has the uke blossomed more than on Internet video sites like YouTube. It fits easily in a Webcam close-up, sounds okay through a cheap computer mic and speakers, and is simple enough to allow just about anyone to share their own song with the whole world. This chapter will help you learn some new strums and chords so you can join the new pop ukulele revolution.

LESSON 1: THE SYNCOPATED STRUM

VIDEO EXAMPLE Syncopation means to shift the emphasis to the offbeat. To show syncopation in written music, dotted rhythms, rests, and ties are sometimes used.

The strum shown below is the Swiss Army knife of strum patterns. It is the universal folk-rock-alternative-swing-funk-punk-campfire strum. This one is good at any speed, fast or slow, swinging or straight. Note the tie that connects the "&" of beat 2 to beat 3, creating a syncopation. Be sure to tap your foot and count out loud.

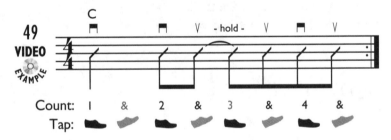

If you find this rhythm a little confusing, break it down into one- or two-beat segments:

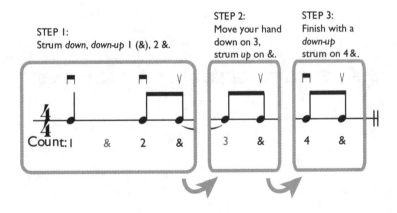

To practice the syncopated strum, here are some exercises that follow the same progression as parts of Train's "Hey, Soul Sister." This progression of diatonic chords goes I-V-vi-IV, a progression that can be heard in countless songs. Remember that in a major key, I, IV, and V are major, while vi is minor. Here it is in the key of C.

VIDEO EXAMPLE MY FEET HURT (OY! SOLE BLISTERS!)

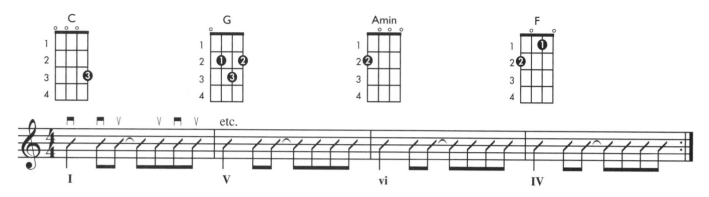

Now try it in G. The vi chord is Emin, which you haven't had a chance to play very much.

VIDEO EXAMPLE AUTOHARP SALE (REPLACE OLD ZITHERS!)

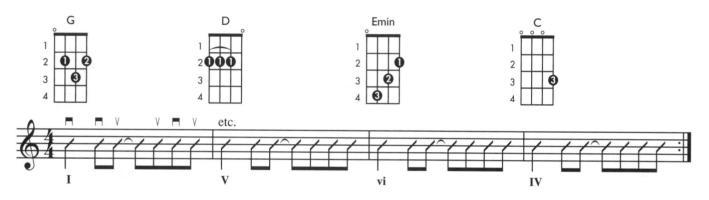

Here's one more I-V-vi-IV progression. This time, the rhythm is in swing eighths and the strum has a slight variation (leaving out the upstroke on the "&" of beat 2). The key is F. This progression introduces the B♭ chord. If the 1st-finger barre gives you trouble, play strings 4, 3, and 2, and let the side of your 1st finger mute the 1st string.

VIDEO EXAMPLE DREAMS OF SUMMER ON A GLOOMY DAY (HAZE, COLD, MISTERS)

Swing 8ths

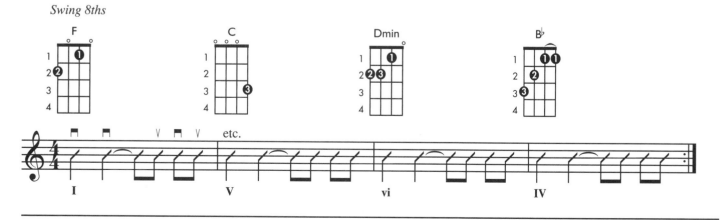

VIDEO

A *mute stroke* is a downstroke where the strings have been muted or damped. All you hear is the percussive snap of the downstroke, but none of the notes of the chord. You can mute the strings with either the right or left hand. Mute strokes allow you to introduce a new texture into your strumming so that you can play more sophisticated grooves. You can even create the impression of more than one instrument playing!

THE RIGHT-HAND MUTE STROKE
By muting the strings with the right hand as you strum down, you can create the loudest form of mute stroke. The right-hand mute stroke works great even if you are strumming chords with open strings. These steps will show you how to do it.

1. First, make sure your left hand is not fingering a chord or touching the strings while you learn how to do the stroke.

2. Now, holding your uke in playing position, place your right-hand palm on the strings, fingers stretched out, covering up the soundhole. Keep your wrist fairly straight so that your hand falls across the strings at a natural angle. (See photo to the right.)

Step 2.

3. Rock your hand backward on the strings so that your thumb sticks up at about a 45 degree angle to the top. The other side of your hand should still be touching the strings. Think of this as the "karate chop" part of your hand. This is the part that mutes the strings. (See photo.)

4. Now that your fingers have some room to move, you should be able to perform a downstroke with your index finger while keeping the strings muted with the "karate chop" part of your hand (see photo). You should hear just a percussive sound. If you hear notes, the muting part of your hand is not doing its job!

Step 3.

5. Repeat the downstroke several times so that you get used to the sound and feel of it. You're not done yet, though!

6. The tricky part is that you need to execute the mute at the same time you are performing a normal downstroke. First, lift your hand off the strings and perform a normal downstroke. Now try it again in slow motion, but this time turn your hand to the right so that the "karate chop" part contacts the strings a fraction of a moment before the index finger does the downstroke. It will take some practice to get the timing just right. Repeat it over and over so that you can do it in one fluid motion.

Step 4.

7. You can do the right-hand mute stroke with the index finger downstroke or with a pick. The motion and basic sound is the same.

MUTE STROKES ON THE BACKBEAT

Remember the backbeat? The backbeat is beats 2 and 4 of a measure of 4 beats (see page 50). In a rock or blues drum pattern, these are the beats where the loud crack of the snare drum is heard. You can use mute strokes (shown with an X on the note head) to simulate the snare drum in a rock beat. Remember, on the mute stroke, you should hear *no notes, only percussion!*

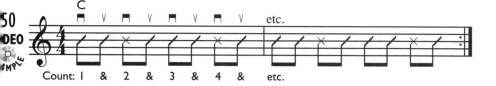

The strum pattern shown above is reminiscent of the guitar grooves used by John Fogerty of Creedence Clearwater Revival. This groove has its roots in Tex-Mex, a Texas hybrid of Mexican traditional music and Texas blues and rock. Following is a progression to practice using your new strum. You can change chords on the beats as written, or you can *anticipate* them by changing chords a half a beat sooner. For example, in the first measure, change to the F chord on the "&" of beat 4. (Note: In the video, Examples 51 and 52 are played using this anticipation technique.)

TRY IT WITH A SWING

If you use the mute stroke with a swing-eighths feel, you get a Jamaican reggae kind of groove. Try the above progression with swing eighths. Then try the one below. It has an additional challenge of switching chords within the measure on bars 2 and 4. You may need to practice these separately before trying the whole progression.

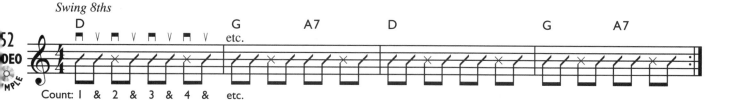

THE LEFT-HAND MUTE STROKE

You can also use your left-hand fingers to create mute strokes. To do this, strum normally and relax the pressure of your fretting fingers on the beats you want muted. This works best on chords that have few open strings, like D and G. You'll be able to use this approach a lot more with the moveable chord forms in the next lesson. Try it with the progressions on this page to hear which chords work better.

LESSON 3: MOVEABLE CHORD FORMS, OR HOW I LEARNED TO BE MY OWN CHORD DICTIONARY IN MY SPARE TIME WITH NO MONEY DOWN!

When you learned your first chords, you were told "here's how to play a C chord; any time you see a C chord in the music, play it like this." You can play a ton of great music just using simple open position major and minor chords. But if you really want to take the lid off of your capabilities, you need *moveable chord forms*.

Moveable chord forms are based on the interval structures and shapes of open-position chords. As these structures move up the neck, they no longer have open strings. When you take open strings out of the equation, you can move any shape to any fret position and get the same type of chord and sound on a new root note.

VIDEO PASSING THE BARRE EXAM

To take advantage of moveable chord forms, you're going to need to be able to play multiple strings with one finger (usually your 1st finger). This is called a *barre*. You may have to barre two, three, or four strings.

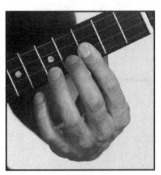 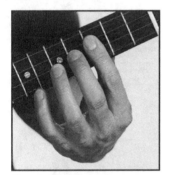 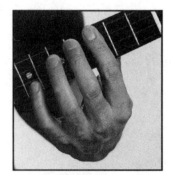

2-string barre.   *3-string barre.*   *4-string barre.*

You have had opportunities to try barres and partial barres throughout this book. If you've been avoiding them or felt like you couldn't make them work, now is the time to prevail! Here are a few tips:

- **The goal of the barre is to get the strings down to the fret!** It doesn't matter how hard you press or how much you grit your teeth if the strings aren't getting to the fret. It shouldn't take too much physical effort, but you need to be aware of what is happening with the strings.

- A barre requires a different finger placement than a normal note. Don't use the tip of your finger, instead use the flat part where your fingerprint is.

- You may need to straighten out your finger and use two joints to cover the strings. Be careful that the little dip at the finger joint doesn't get placed on a string, or that string might not get pressed down.

- You may also need to shift your finger up or down, or roll your finger slightly to one side or another to get the notes to sound.

- Above all, be patient and persistent. Try practicing barres for a few minutes every day. It's amazing what you can do if you give things time to develop!

THE A FORM MOVEABLE CHORDS

Let's start your exploration of moveable forms with forms based on open A chords. Below are the variations of A chords you have worked with so far: A Major, A Minor, and two fingerings of A7. Underneath each diagram, the chord tones are labeled.

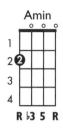

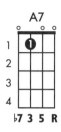

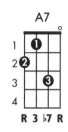

R =	root
3 =	3rd (major 3rd)
♭3 =	minor 3rd
5 =	5th
♭7 =	minor 7th

Following are the same chord forms moved up one half step (one position) to form chords in B♭. Look at the first chord (B♭ Major) and compare it with A Major above. Each note on the 3rd and 4th string have been moved up one half step, with the fingering changed to the 3rd and 2nd finger. This frees up the 1st finger to barre strings 1 and 2 at the 1st fret. These notes were open in the A Major chord but need to be on the 1st fret in the B♭ chord. The structure of roots, 3rds, and 5ths is identical. Try learning and comparing all the fingerings.

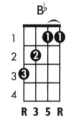

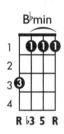

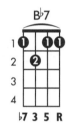

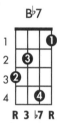

We'll call these fingerings the *A form* chords because they are based on the structures used for the open A chords. The fingerings for the B♭ chords can continue to be moved up the neck to make new chords based on the A forms. You can follow the root notes up the A string (1st string) to find all of the new chords (see chart below). For example, if you put your 1st finger at the 5th fret and build the minor chord fingering shown above, you'll have a D Minor chord.

The A Form Chords by Position (Root on String 1)

Here are the chords you get by moving the A form up the neck. The fret positions indicate the position of the barre finger. If you use the minor shape, you get minor chords. If you use the dominant 7th shapes, you get dominant 7th chords. Try starting at the 1st fret with any fingering, and name the chords as you move up one fret at a time.

Fret position:		1st	2nd	3rd	4th	5th	6th	7th	8th	9th	10th	11th
Chord:	A	A#/ B♭	B	C	C#/ D♭	D	D#/ E♭	E	F	F#/ G♭	G	G#/ A♭

Note: Depending on how many frets your uke has, you may not be able to move the position past the 9th or 10th fret.

THE C FORM MOVEABLE CHORDS

Below are the open C and C7 chords, with the chord tones shown underneath. Since the 3rd of the chord is on the open 2nd string, and therefore can't be lowered to a minor 3rd, we won't have a minor fingering in this set. To the right of the C chords are the corresponding D chords you get by moving the C chords up one whole step. The barred 1st finger replaces the notes that were open in the C chords.

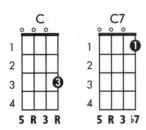
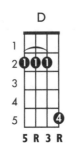
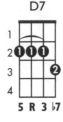

The C Form Chords by Position (Root on String 3)

Here are the chords you get by moving the C form up the neck. The root of this form is on the 3rd string.

Fret position:		1st	2nd	3rd	4th	5th	6th	7th	8th	9th	10th	11th
Chord:	C	C#/Db	D	D#/Eb	E	F	F#/Gb	G	G#/Ab	A	A#/Bb	B

THE F FORM MOVEABLE CHORDS

Now, let's look at the F forms. Below is the open F chord plus two fingerings of F7. F Minor can be played in open position but it requires a few changes to the structure so we'll leave it out for now. Compare the F chord fingerings to the G chords you get by moving the F chords up one whole step.

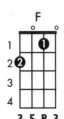
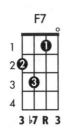
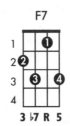
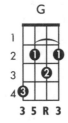
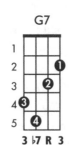
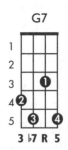

The F Form Chords by Position (Root on String 2)

Here are the chords you get by moving the F form up the neck. The fret positions indicate the position of the root note on the 2nd string. Note that this form has notes that are lower on the neck than the position of the root note, so *the root note position does not equal the position of the barre.*

Fret position:	1st	2nd	3rd	4th	5th	6th	7th	8th	9th	10th	11th	12th
Chord:	F	F#/Gb	G	G#/Ab	A	A#/Bb	B	C	C#/Db	D	D#/Eb	E

THE G FORM MOVEABLE CHORDS

Here are fingerings for G, G Minor, and G7, followed by the moveable fingerings you get if you move the G chords up one whole step.

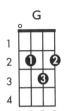
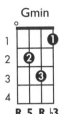
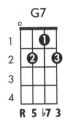
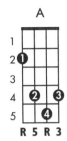
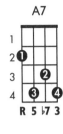
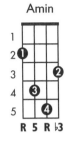

G — **R 5 R 3**

Gmin — **R 5 R ♭3**

G7 — **R 5 ♭7 3**

A — **R 5 R 3**

Amin — **R 5 R ♭3**

A7 — **R 5 ♭7 3**

SUPER UKE TIP

Sometimes, we don't play or finger all of the available notes in a chord. For example, it would be very common (and easier) to finger and play only the first three strings of the A chords shown. You have to remember where your root is!

The G Form Chords by Position (Root on String 4)

Here are the chords you get by moving the G form up the neck. The root of these forms is on the 4th string.

Fret position:		1st	2nd	3rd	4th	5th	6th	7th	8th	9th	10th	11th
Chord:		G	G#/Ab	A	A#/Bb	B	C	C#/Db	D	D#/Eb	E	F	F#/Gb

THE D FORM MOVEABLE CHORDS

The last form we'll look at is based on D chords. Here are D, D Minor, and D7, followed by E, E Minor, and E7 with the same structures moved up a whole step. You may remember another fingering for D7 that appeared with the C form chords. Some of the forms do overlap in parts of their shapes.

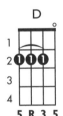
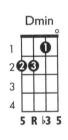
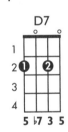
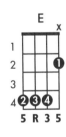
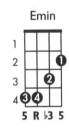
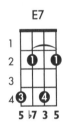

D — **5 R 3 5**

Dmin — **5 R ♭3 5**

D7 — **5 ♭7 3 5**

E — **5 R 3 5**

Emin — **5 R ♭3 5**

E7 — **5 ♭7 3 5**

The D Form Chords by Position (Root on String 2)

Here are the chords you get by moving the D form up the neck. The root for the D and D Minor forms is on the 2nd string. The D7 form is tricky, because it doesn't have the root in this fingering. The best way to keep track is to visualize the D Major form to find the position of the chord you are looking for, then make the necessary fingering changes to get the dominant 7th form of that chord.

Fret position:	2nd	3rd	4th	5th	6th	7th	8th	9th	10th	11th	12th	13th
Chord:	D	D#/Eb	E	F	F#/Gb	G	G#/Ab	A	A#/Bb	B	C	C#/Db

This lesson will make use of your new moveable chord shapes and recombine some of your strumming techniques to get new grooves.

THE REGGAE BEAT, SCRATCHING, AND SQUEEZING

Reggae music originated in Jamaica in the 1960s and became a worldwide phenomenon in the 1970s with artists like Bob Marley, Peter Tosh, and Jimmy Cliff. Reggae's influence continues both as a vehicle for political expression and in the laid-back grooves of artists like Jack Johnson and Jason Mraz.

The rhythm guitar of Bob Marley established one of the most imitated grooves of all time. The trick is to use moveable chord forms so there are no open strings. The mute strokes (indicated by an "X" on the note head) are made by relaxing the finger pressure of the left hand without lifting the fingers off the strings. The mute strokes are "scratching." The following groove scratches on beats1 and 3, while squeezing the chord on beats 2 and 4. Think "scratch, squeeze, scratch, squeeze." Don't forget to swing the eighths!

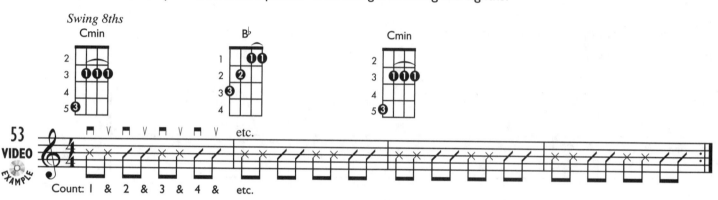

Here's another chance to work with the reggae groove. You'll be playing in the key of B♭, using chord shapes from the A form and D form. The E♭ and F chords shown might give you trouble depending on your particular fingers. It's perfectly okay to just play strings 2, 3, and 4 on these chords, leaving the 1st string muted so you can focus your effort on the 3rd-finger barre. Note that in measures 2, 4, and 6, you have to change chords within the measure—but you're just moving the same form up or down two frets.

VIDEO EXAMPLE WHO WANTS A COOL BEVERAGE?

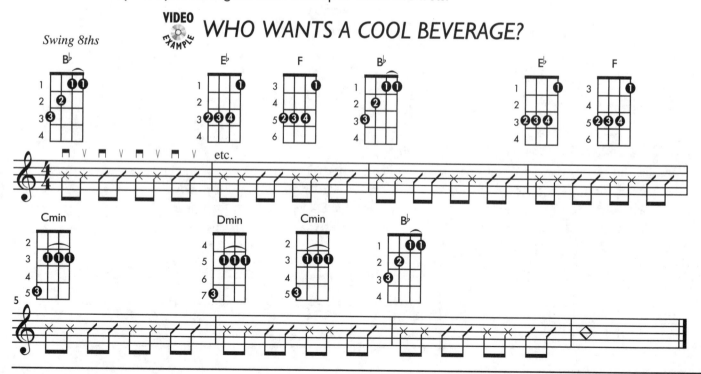

The next exercise uses scratch strokes in a different part of the groove. This strum pattern has more space in it, beginning with a half note followed by a staccato quarter note, then eighth-note mute strokes. The eighth notes are straight (not swung) and the groove has an old-school gospel/soul feel like the music of Curtis Mayfield. The groove changes up to a simple strum on the third line. "Uke Got Soul" is in the key of D Major and uses moveable chord shapes from the C form, A form, F form, and G form.

UKE GOT SOUL

CHAPTER 8

Taking It Home: Island Style

The Hawaiian style of ukulele is full of variety and continues to evolve in the present through young modern players like Herb Ohta, Jr. and Daniel Ho. Hawaiian music comes in many flavors and rhythms, from the swing-influenced Hapa Haole songs of the '20s and '30s to the rolling fingerpicked guitar style known as "slack-key." If you dig deep into the Hawaiian repertoire, you will find that songs are often presented in many different styles and tempos. Overall, the Hawaiian ukulele style prizes beautiful tone, delicately textured rhythms, and a sense of ebb and flow that recalls the natural beauty of the islands and the surrounding ocean.

If you were to only learn one Hawaiian song, a good choice is *Aloha 'Oe*, composed in 1878 by Queen Lili'uokalani, the last monarch of Hawaii. The melody shows the influence of Christian hymns brought to the islands by missionaries in the 1800s. The lyrics tell of a parting embrace, which has come to symbolize longing for loved ones and for homeland. There are countless recordings, from Hawaiian steel guitarists to Elvis.

The following arrangement in the key of F shows both the melody and the chords. Try strumming it first in a slow walking tempo with straight-eighth notes, using the rhythm you learned on page 21. Also, try it using swing eighths or with other strum patterns you have used. You can use the standard notation or the TAB to learn the melody, which consists of a 16-measure verse and a 16-measure chorus. The phrase marks (page 92) show that the verse and chorus each consist of four phrases of about 4 bars each. Here are the chord shapes you'll need:

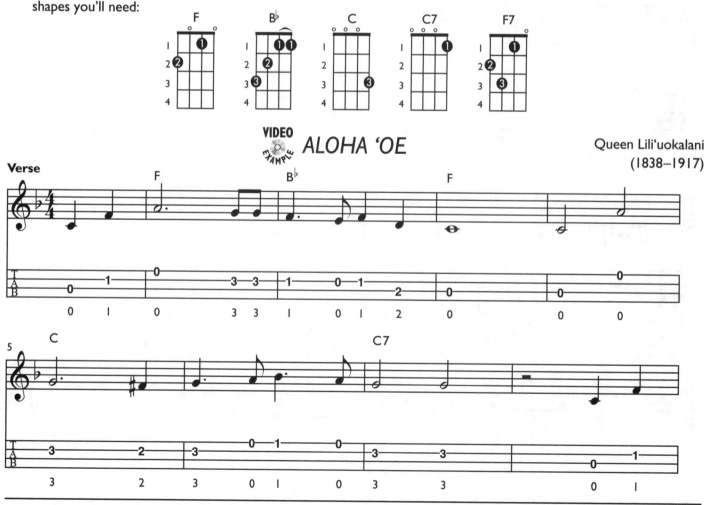

VIDEO EXAMPLE

ALOHA 'OE

Queen Lili'uokalani
(1838–1917)

In this lesson, you will learn a few new strums that fit nicely with a swing-eighths groove for Hawaiian-style songs. First, start by strumming and counting basic swing eighths with the index finger. Take notice of the "&" of beats 2 and 4 (marked with *). You'll be doing something special with these soon.

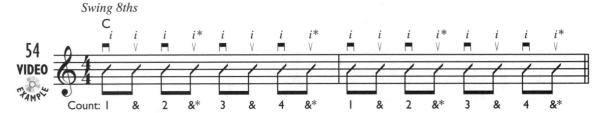

ROLLING WITH A RAKE

One technique that adds texture is to *roll* the chord on certain beats within the pattern. Each normal stroke should sound like all the strings are hit at once but a roll sounds like the notes of the chord come out very quickly one after the other. There are many ways to accomplish this effect. The simplest way to roll the chord is called a *rake*. This is done by dragging the finger through the strings so that they sound one at a time but still quickly enough that they ring together as a chord on the beat. A rake can be a downstroke or an upstroke depending on the beat on which it falls. Try adding a rake on the "&" of 2 and the "&" of 4 in your strum pattern. These will be upstroke rakes.

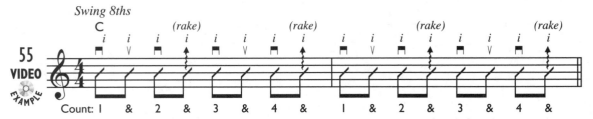

THE ALTERNATING TRIPLE STRUM

Another strumming groove for swing eighths incorporates one of the triple strums you learned on page 59. Here, the triple strum produces a triplet rhythm on beats 2 and 4. This triple strum is a downstroke with *i*, followed by another downstroke with the thumb (*T*), and then an upstroke with *i*.

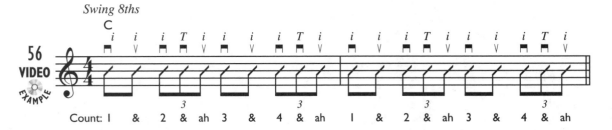

ALTERNATING TRIPLE WITH A RAKE

Once you're very comfortable with the above strums, try adding rakes to the alternating triple strum. Go slowly and count the beats. This strum was inspired by some advanced strums used by ukulele player and falsetto singing master Richard Hoʻopiʻi (pronounced Ho-OH-pee-ee) and other players.

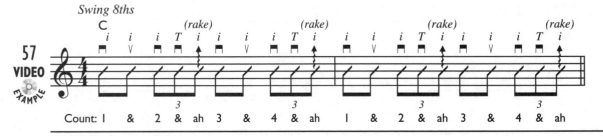

Here's a short strumming tune that pays tribute to the style of Richard Ho'opi'i. The song is in the key of C and begins with a two-bar vamp of D7, G7, and C. The *vamp* is a common introduction for songs that accompany traditional Hawaiian hula dancing. It can be repeated as many times as desired before the rest of the song starts. The eight beats of the vamp match up with the eight counts of the hula dance step called the *kaholo*, used at the introduction of hula dances.

This song will introduce you to some new chords, such as Csus4 (an abbreviation for the full name "C suspended fourth"), F Minor (Fmin), and new voicings for D7 and G7. You can try all of the new techniques as shown, or use simpler strums and familiar voicings of the chords.

VIDEO EXAMPLE — HULA FOR HO'OPI'I

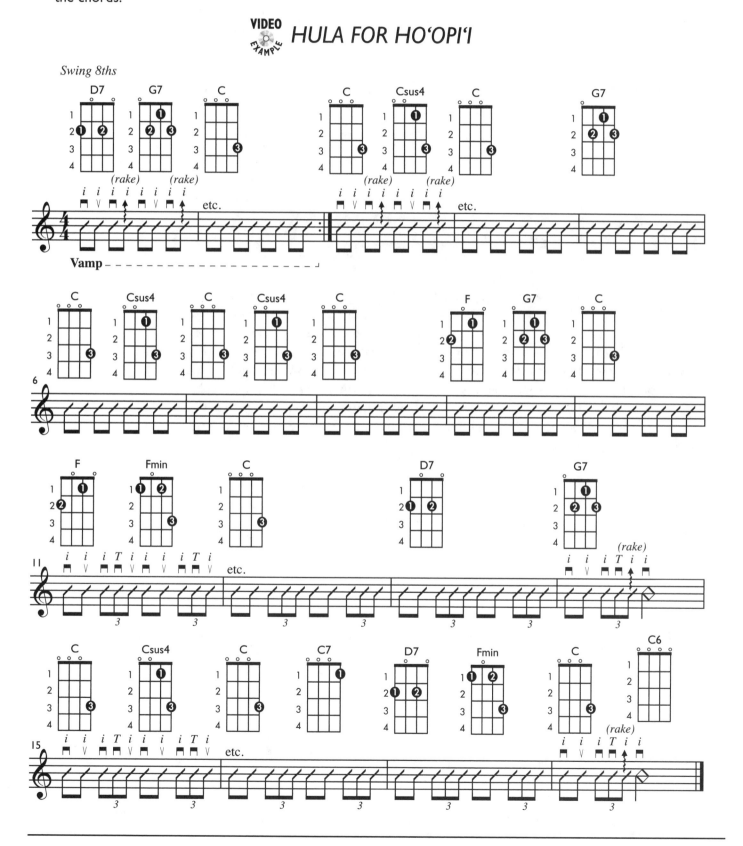

CHAPTER 9

Ukulele Blues

The blues is so much a part of American music that its influence is felt in nearly every style. Far more than just the feeling of "good times that done gone bad," the blues is:

- A musical style
- A form of poetry
- A type of scale
- An attitude
- A specific musical form and chord progression
- An incurable, infectious human condition that is both miserable and joyful at the same time

LESSON 1: THE 12-BAR BLUES

THE FORM

The *12-bar blues* is one of the most basic song *forms*. Remember, the form is the organization, or structure, of a piece. The 12-bar blues derives its name from the number of measures (bars) in the form. Below is a common version of the 12-bar blues in the key of A. Included are chord symbols and Roman numerals indicating the analysis of the harmony. Try it with either simple downstrokes or one of the swing-eighths strums you learned on page 53. You can play this progression using the simple major chords shown, or you can replace each chord with dominant 7ths (A7, D7, E7). The blues progression is unusual in that it sounds good to use dominant 7ths on all chords, not just the V chord. Fingerings for these chords are on page 55.

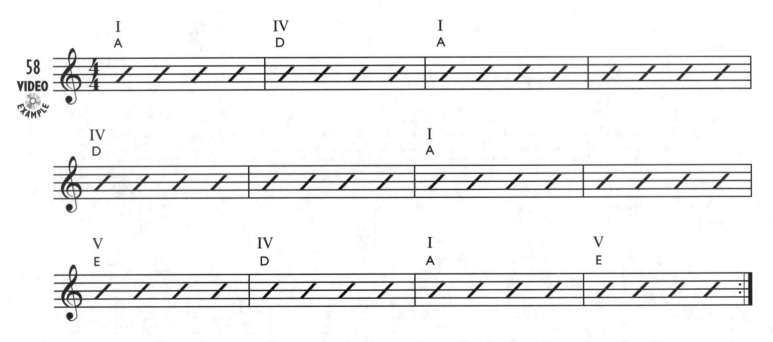

LESSON 2: MEMORIZING THE 12-BAR BLUES

There may be times when you want to play with other people who don't know the same songs you do. The 12-bar blues is widely known by musicians at all levels of experience. A working knowledge of how to play through the progression, as well as improvising on it, can give you an "ace up your sleeve" in those difficult situations when you can't decide what to jam on.

BLUES POETRY

The 12-bar blues is organized in three lines of four measures each. This mirrors the poetic form of many blues lyrics. A common form of blues lyric consists of a statement (line 1), a repetition of the statement (line 2), and a sort of "clincher" (line 3). Check out these common blues verses:

> *My baby just left me, and man I feel so bad*
> *My baby just left me, and man I feel so bad*
> *Since my baby left me, I lost everything I had*

> *I'd rather drink muddy water, sleep in a hollow log*
> *I'd rather drink muddy water, sleep in a hollow log*
> *Than stay in this city, treated like a dirty dog*

PLAY BY NUMBERS

You may have noticed that the blues contains the three primary chords discussed on page 47. These are the I, IV, and V chords. In the key of A, these would be:

$$I = A \qquad IV = D \qquad V = E$$

Try to memorize the progression using these numbers. That way, you will learn its structure without being limited to the key of A. Soon, you will be able play the blues in any key, as long as you know what the I, IV, and V chords are for that key. To make it easier, memorize one line at a time.

PLAY IT IN YOUR SLEEP

To get the most out of learning the blues, try to memorize the progression. Be able to play it over and over without losing your place in the form. This will make it much easier to jam with other players. You will be able to enjoy the musical interaction of the moment without worrying about whether you brought your music or whether you are on bar 10 or bar 6.

In addition, you should know there are many possible variations on the 12-bar blues form. Some have more chords, some have fewer, and some have different chords substituted for the common ones. By burning a specific, basic version of the pattern into your brain through repetition and study, you will have an easier time compensating for slight variations from song to song.

The blues progression can be played to just about any rhythm you can imagine. One of the classic rhythms, particularly associated with Chicago blues, is the *shuffle*. In music, the word shuffle can mean different things to different people. For example, to a fiddler, a shuffle is a particular type of bowing pattern. To a blues player, a shuffle is a type of groove played in the swing-eighths feel. There is, of course, an exception. A "straight shuffle" uses the same patterns you are learning here but with a straight-eighths (un-swung) feel.

VIDEO PLAYING THE SHUFFLE

The following shuffle pattern is based on patterns you hear from rhythm guitar players or the left hand of a blues piano player. This type of shuffle starts with a major chord on the first two eighth notes, then moves the 5th of the chord up a whole step to the 6th for two eighth notes.

Below, the shuffle pattern is shown for each chord you will need in the key of A. Practice each pattern separately for several bars. In blues rhythm, chords can be played as full triads, or as just the root with the 5th (alternating with the 6th), as is shown for the D and E chords. To give it a more authoritative sound, use all downstrokes instead of alternating down-up.

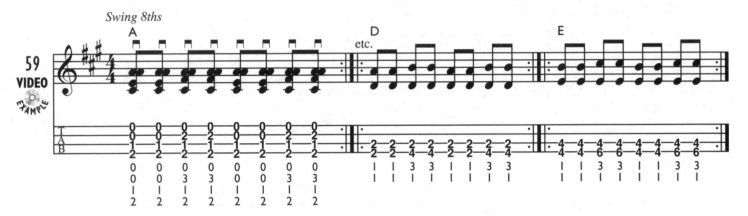

Here are a few more tidbits about playing the shuffle:

* These shuffle patterns above represent the concept of *playing a pattern that represents a single chord*. Even though, technically, you are alternating between, say, A and A6, the pattern functions in the same way as an unchanging A chord. Sometimes in the blues, single-note riffs or even tiny progressions are used to represent each chord.

* When you are playing the D and E shuffles, you have to press down both the 3rd and 4th strings with your 1st finger (barre). To do this, remember to use the flat part of your finger (where your fingerprint is) instead of the tip.

* On the D and E chords, you can use the 2nd finger instead of the 3rd if it works better for you.

Here is the whole 12-bar blues form in the key of A, using the shuffle patterns you just learned. The chord analysis (I, IV, V) is shown under the standard notation. Remember, if you get tired of the shuffle rhythm, you can play any versions of A, A7, D, D7, E, or E7 in place of the shuffle pattern for those chords.

WHY DOESN'T IT END ON THE I CHORD?
This 12-bar blues progression ends on the E chord (the V). The V chord doesn't sound like a final resting place for the progression. Rather, the V chord makes it sound like it should repeat. When you have jammed through the form as many times as you want to, you can add one more simple A chord after the 12th measure to give your blues a sense of "coming home to the I chord."

VIDEO EXAMPLE *SHUFFLIN' THROUGH THE BLUES IN A*

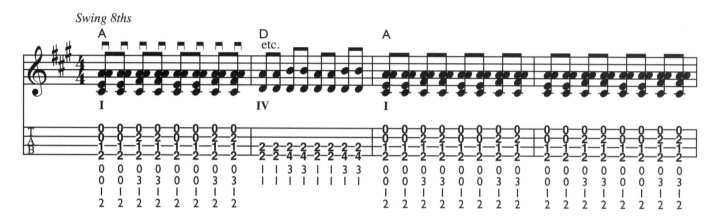

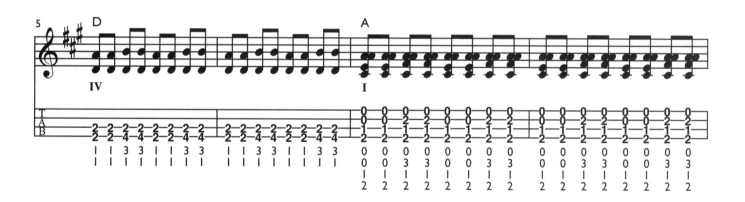

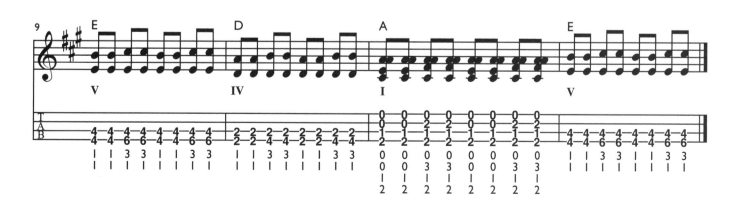

Many blues melodies and solos use the notes of the *minor pentatonic scale*. Unlike the major scale (page 42), which has seven different notes, the minor pentatonic scale has only five different notes (*penta* is the Greek word meaning "five"). Pentatonic scales are very common in folk and traditional music from many cultures around the world.

SCALE DEGREES OF THE MINOR PENTATONIC

Remember back on page 42 when you learned that the major scale can be used to help us understand other scales? Below is a comparison of the notes and scale degrees of an A Major scale and an A Minor Pentatonic scale. The notes and scale degrees show us the differences. The minor pentatonic scale leaves out scale degrees 2 and 6, and lowers the 3rd and 7th by one half step.

VIDEO EXAMPLE

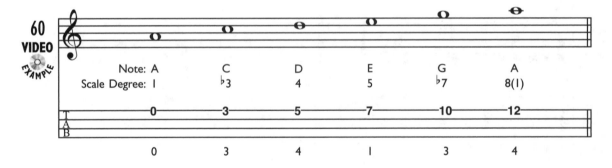

	1	2	3	4	5	6	7
A Major Scale:	A	B	C♯	D	E	F♯	G♯

	1		♭3	4	5		♭7
A Minor Pentatonic Scale:	A		C	D	E		G

THE MINOR PENTATONIC SCALE IN THE KEY OF A ON ONE STRING

Below is the A Minor pentatonic scale shown on the 1st string. You can use any fingering you like. Once you have learned to go up and down the scale, try making up melodies and riffs. Play long and short notes, repeat notes and groups of notes, skip around—do anything to make it sound like music. For fun, try improvising with these notes while the recording of "Shufflin' Through the Blues in A" from page 79 plays in the background.

60
VIDEO EXAMPLE

Note:	A	C	D	E	G	A
Scale Degree:	1	♭3	4	5	♭7	8(1)
TAB:	0	3	5	7	10	12
	0	3	4	1	3	4

VIDEO EXAMPLE **BLUE NOTES**

When a scale has a lowered 3rd degree (♭3), it is said to be a *minor scale*. The cool thing about the blues is that, while the chords are often major, the melody is often minor. This creates a funky, slightly *dissonant* (clashing) sound between the major chords and the minor melody, giving the blues its melancholy, expressive sound.

The minor pentatonic scale contains both the ♭3 and ♭7. These notes help us approximate the sound of old African scales that lie at the core of the blues. When these minor scale notes are played against major chords, they are called *blue notes*. Sometimes blue notes are "bent" out of tune a bit to make them even more expressive. You will learn about string bending in *Intermediate Ukulele*.

THE MINOR PENTATONIC SCALE IN A (OPEN POSITION)

The A Minor Pentatonic scale can also be played in open position. The only tricky thing is that our ukulele tuning only goes down to C, so we have to imagine the low A at the root of the scale. You can substitute the A an octave above (on the open 1st string, or 2nd fret, 4th string). Here are the notes and scale degrees, including an imaginary low A.

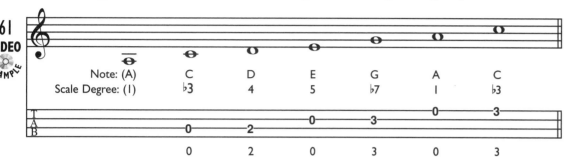

LEARNING TO IMPROVISE

The point of learning the minor pentatonic scale is to use it as a tool for improvising solos. Here are a few tips to get you going.

- When it's your time to solo, remember that you don't have to play a constant stream of notes. Leave some space and choose your moments.

- A *phrase* is like a musical sentence. It has a beginning, middle, and end. A phrase doesn't have to jump immediately into more notes. Imagine that you are inserting commas, periods, question marks, and exclamation points into your solo. This is called *phrasing* (for more, see page 92).

- Repetition is your friend. Repetition is your friend. Repetition creates something familiar for the listener so that when it changes, it has more meaning (like this sentence). You can repeat a note, a phrase, or a rhythmic idea.

- Your other best friend is the tonic note of the scale (note number 1). In the blues, the tonic note works with any of the chords. Even though it is not part of the V chord, it signals that the V chord is heading toward a chord with the tonic note in it. Any time you feel lost, go back and play the tonic note and let it hang for a moment. It's like a reset button for your solo. If you end phrases with a good strong tonic note, they will sound defined and resolved. Later on, you will learn how to creatively work with the other notes, but first, make friends with the tonic!

Here are a couple of short *licks* (mini-phrases) to get you started. Each one ends with the tonic note. Try these when you improvise over the blues progression. You can even try repeating licks like these over and over while the chords change underneath.

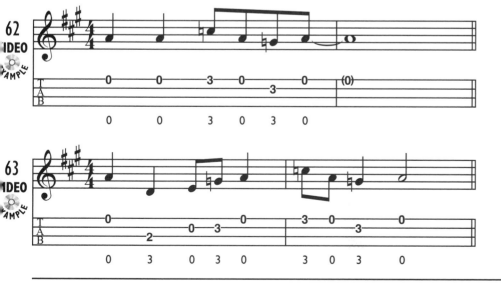

LESSON 5: TRANSPOSITION

Transposing means changing the key of a song.

  WHY TRANSPOSE?

The most common reason for transposing a song to a new key is to better fit the vocal range of a singer. For example, imagine a song in the key of G Major. If this key is too low, you could transpose up to A or even B. Another reason to transpose is to make a melody or chord progression easier to play on the ukulele.

THE SUBSTITUTION METHOD

This method of transposition is the easiest to learn but not the most efficient. First, consider the following progression in G Major. Use simple downstrokes.

Transposing from G Major to D Major

First, you must know how far the new key is from the original key. The key of D is a perfect 5th (P5, seven half steps, seven frets) higher than the key of G. To transpose the song, substitute each of the original chords with the chord a perfect 5th higher:

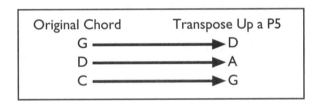

Here is the above progression transposed to D Major.

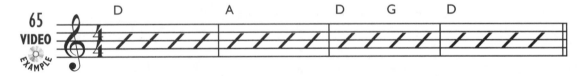

Transposing from G Major to A Major

Try using this method for yourself. Transpose the G Major progression above to the key of A and write in your answers. The answers are at the end of the lesson on page 83.

    1. How far above G is A?
    2. What is the new chord progression?

Transpose this example to the key of A (write in your answers):

THE CHORD ANALYSIS METHOD

At first, this method takes more practice and thought, but eventually you will be able to transpose songs without having to write out the new chords.

Here is an example progression in the key of D Major.

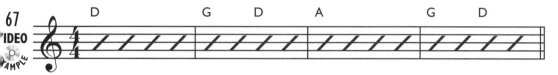

Transposing From D Major to G Major

First, analyze the chord progression with Roman numerals (page 46).

Now you are ready to transpose to any key. Try the key of G Major.

Key of G: I = G   IV = C   V = D

Transposing from D Major to A Major

Try this one yourself (the correct answer is at the bottom of this page).

1. What are the primary chords in the key of A Major?   I = ___   IV = ___   V = ___

Answers to Examples 66 and 70:

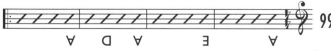

LESSON 6: TRANSPOSING THE BLUES AND THE MINOR PENTATONIC SCALE

Now that you have learned some of the basics of transposition, you can apply them to the blues. By now, you should have the blues progression memorized by chord number (I, IV, and V). This is useful because you never know what key someone might want to play in when you're in a jamming situation.

Let's say you want to play a 12-bar blues in C. First, you need the I, IV, and V chords in the key of C. You can either name them by memory or find them by counting up the C Major scale.

Key: C Major   I = C   IV = F   V = G

You can plug those chords into the 12-bar blues formula you learned on page 76.

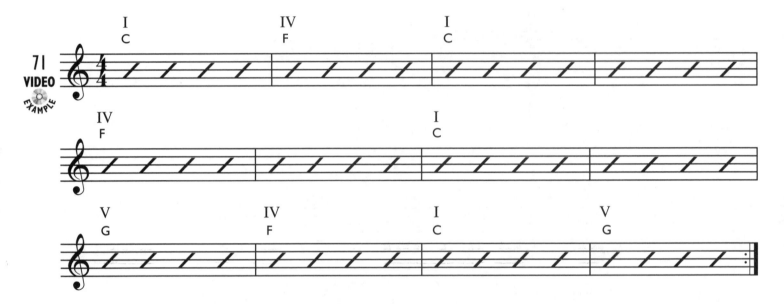

Now that you know what the chord progression is, you can choose the chord voicings and groove you might use to play it. Here are some options:

- The easiest option is to play the major chords in open position with simple downstrokes. Elegant and tasteful!

- You can use dominant 7th chords for each chord in the progression. Simply change C, F, and G to C7, F7, and G7.

- Try some of the different strum patterns, grooves, and swing-eighth/straight-eighth feels you have learned.

If you're up for a new challenge, try some moveable forms for dominant 7th chords. Give these fingerings a spin, then plug them into the 12-bar blues in C shown below with a staccato swing strum.

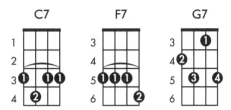

12-BAR BLUES IN C (A BOUNCY C!)

SUPER UKE TIP: MOVEABLE CHORDS MAKE FOR EASY TRANSPOSITION

If you learned the 12-bar blues in C using the moveable chords shown above, you can easily transpose to nearby keys by moving all the shapes up or down on the neck. For example, if you wanted to play the 12-bar blues in the key of D, just move the whole set of chords up one whole step (two frets).

You can also transpose the minor pentatonic scale to a new key. The easiest way to do this is to treat the scale fingering as a moveable shape. You learned the minor pentatonic scale in A. The key of C is a minor 3rd (three frets) higher than A. If you move all of the notes from the A Minor Pentatonic scale up three frets, you will have the C Minor Pentatonic scale. You get a bonus note in this key: the tonic note of C is available on the open 3rd string. Use this scale to improvise riffs and solos over "12-Bar Blues in C (A Bouncy C!)."

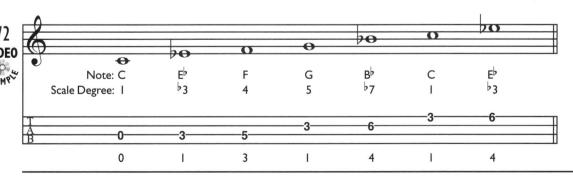

THE NATURAL MINOR SCALE IN A

Technically, any scale that has a minor 3rd ($\flat$3) is considered minor. There is one particular scale that is called the *natural minor scale*. Here it is in the key of A on the 1st string.

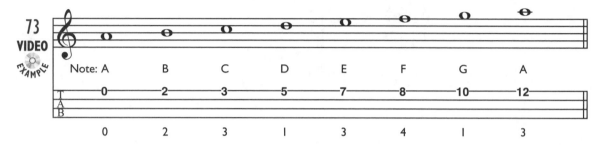

Following are a few things to notice about the natural minor scale.

Relative Minor (A Minor) and Relative Major (C Major)

In the key of A, the natural minor scale has no sharps and flats. It has the same notes and key signature as the key of C Major. We say that A Minor is the *relative minor* of C Major. The relative minor is always the scale whose root is the 6th note of the relative major.

Characteristic Notes: $\flat$3rd, $\flat$6th, and $\flat$7th

Let's compare the A Natural Minor scale with the A Major scale to see what is different. The 3rd, 6th, and 7th degrees are all a half step lower ($\flat$3, $\flat$6, and $\flat$7).

A Major Scale:	A	B	C#	D	E	F#	G#	A
Scale degrees:	1	2	3	4	5	6	7	8(1)
A Natural Minor Scale:	A	B	C	D	E	F	G	A
Scale degrees:	1	2	$\flat$3	4	5	$\flat$6	$\flat$7	8(1)

The Primary Chords Are All Minor (i, iv, v)

If we build triads on the 1st, 4th, and 5th degrees using only the notes of the natural minor scale, we get i, iv, and v chords that are all minor. Fun fact: There are other minor scales that have different qualities on the IV and V chords, but those scales are also named differently.

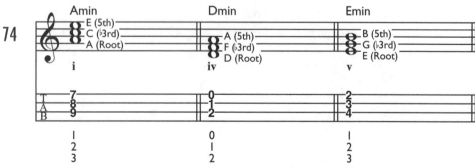

Here is a 12-bar blues progression in the key of A Minor. Note that the last measure stays on A Minor instead of going to the v chord of E Minor. Variations like this are common in blues progressions.

NUNMOOR BLUES: A 12-BAR BLUES IN A MINOR

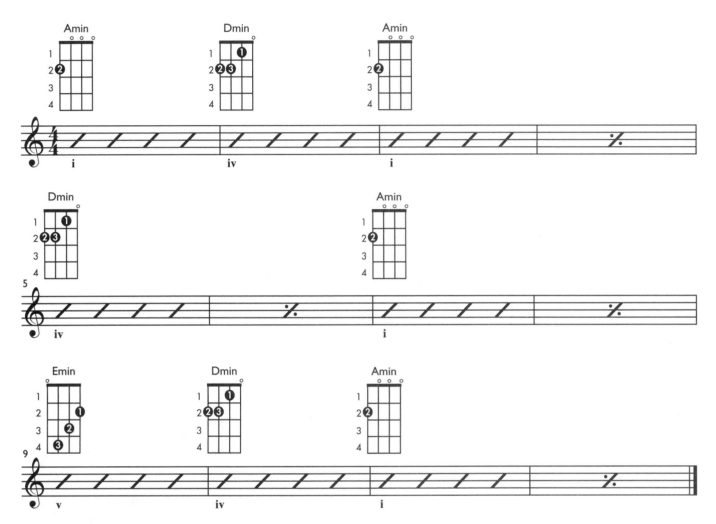

IMPROVISING ON A MINOR BLUES

The good news about playing in minor keys is that you can still use the minor pentatonic scale. In fact, it is more closely tied to the harmony of a minor key than it is to a major key. You can also fill in the missing 2nd and ♭6th degrees to make it a natural minor scale. Below is the A Minor pentatonic followed by the A Natural Minor in open position. Notice the imaginary low A and B notes that are needed to make the scale appear complete. These notes can be replaced with their counterparts an octave higher. Listen to the recording of the blues progression shown above and use it as a backing track to practice soloing.

CHAPTER 10

Introduction to Fingerstyle

LESSON 1: THE RIGHT-HAND POSITION

Fingerstyle, or *fingerpicking,* means playing the ukulele with the right-hand fingers and thumb, using one digit per string. Many great ukulele players have incorporated fingerstyle into their playing. John King, for example, used classical techniques to bring the music of Bach to the uke. Others use fingerstyle to play folk, blues, or jazz.

RIGHT-HAND FINGERS

There are many stringed instruments played fingerstyle, so there are different systems for naming the right-hand fingers. Classical guitarists use abbreviations of the Spanish names for the fingers: *p, i, m, a* (*p* = thumb, *i* = index, *m* = middle, *a* = ring). The ukulele has many playing styles, including thumb style, which designates the thumb as *T*. Since we have already used *T* for the thumb, we will continue to use it throughout this method.

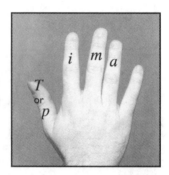

HOME POSITION

You will begin your exploration of fingerpicking by assigning each finger to one string. This may change later on, but it's a good place to start.

 VIDEO
EXAMPLE

- *T* plays the 4th string.
- *i* plays the 3rd string.
- *m* plays the 2nd string.
- *a* plays the 1st string.

T = Thumb
i = index finger
m = middle finger
a = ring finger

Fingerstyle "home position."

THE RIGHT-HAND WRIST

To achieve the best technical fluency possible (to maximize tone and minimize stress), it is helpful to understand some basic terms regarding the wrist:

Arch
(up-and-down motion)

Rotation
(side-to-side motion)

Tilt
(Left-to-right motion from the elbow)

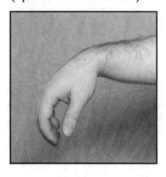

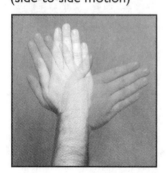

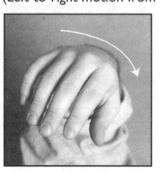

Your wrist should have a slight arch, little or no rotation, and perhaps a slight tilt in toward your thumb. Keep your fingers relaxed and avoid tension in your forearm. If you feel tension or tightness, stop and "shake it out."

LESSON 2: ARPEGGIO PATTERN *T-i-m-a*

A good way to start fingerpicking is to learn a few repetitive patterns. These can be used with any chords you know. By placing your fingers in "home position," you can concentrate on which finger to play without worrying about which string to play.

If you find yourself getting tripped up, remove your hand from the ukulele. Hold it up in the air and practice moving the fingers to the pattern while saying the right-hand pattern aloud a few times (for example: *T-i-m-a, T-i-m-a,* etc.). Then go back to the uke and try again.

The pattern on this page is called an *arpeggio*. An arpeggio is the notes of a chord sounded one at a time. They can be played ascending, descending, or in a more complex pattern. The reentrant 4th string of the uke adds complexity to the sound of the arpeggio pattern, even though the finger pattern is very simple. The pattern you will play goes "thumb-index-middle-ring," or *T-i-m-a.* The progression shown uses C, F, and G7 chords, but you can try this pattern with any chord progression. You may want to practice the pattern with each chord individually for a while before putting the song together.

This progression comes from a Hawaiian song named "Hi'ilawe" (pronounced "he-ee-LAH-vey"), written in the 1880s. This song is a standard among slack-key guitarists. Slack-key master Gabby Pahinui (1921–1980) made "Hi'ilawe" one of his signature songs.

VIDEO EXAMPLE *HI'ILAWE*

Sam Li`a Kalainaina, Sr.

LESSON 3: MIDDLE AND RING FINGERS TOGETHER

The pattern in this lesson goes "thumb-index-middle/ring-index," or *T-i-ma-i*. Your right-hand fingers will be in the same home position as the last lesson. The difference is that now your middle and ring fingers will play simultaneously. You can warm up for this pattern by tapping your fingers on a table. Try to get *m* and *a* to synchronize so they move as one. The following progression is in the key of G, but you can also try the pattern with other chords or the song from the previous lesson. The first iteration of the pattern has been highlighted to make it easier to see.

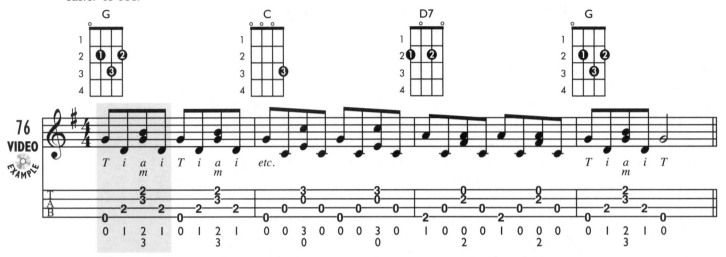

LESSON 4: FINGERPICKING IN $\frac{3}{4}$

You can use a variation of the above pattern to fingerpick progressions in waltz time ($\frac{3}{4}$). Since the last pattern was actually two beats long, all you have to do is add two extra eighth notes to make the pattern three beats long.

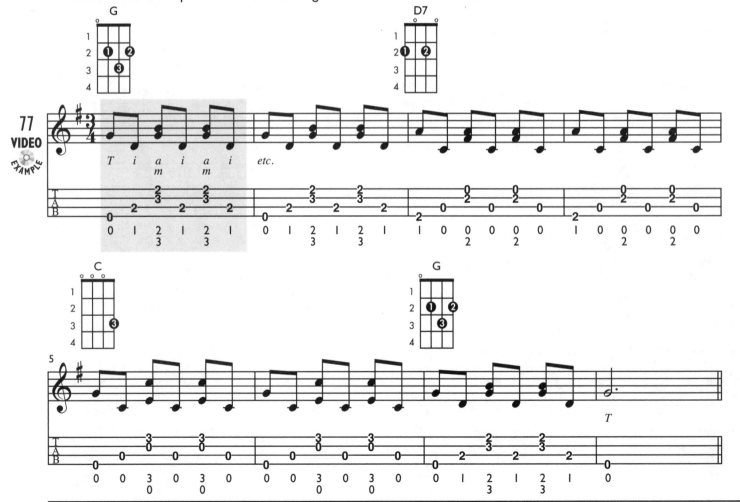

A CHANGE IN HOME POSITION

In alternating-thumb patterns, the thumb moves back and forth between two strings. You will have to change your home position so that the thumb can be in charge of both the 3rd and 4th strings. The index finger will play string 2, and the middle finger will play string 1. The ring finger can go for drinks.

Here is the pattern slowed down to quarter notes to make it easier to learn. The chords alternate between C and C6.

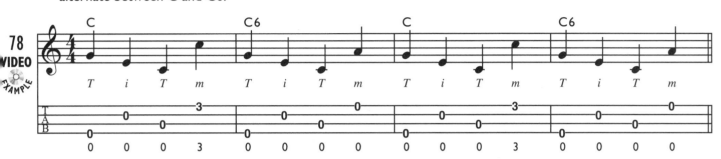

The fun thing about the alternating-thumb pattern is that when it combines with the reentrant tuning, it begins to play tricks on your ears. It's hard to tell where the pattern starts and stops. Try this solo fingerstyle piece. If you stay focused on the picking pattern, you won't get lost. There are a couple of new chords and voicings that give a sense of melody to the progression. Don't forget the repeats!

UKALEIDOSCOPE

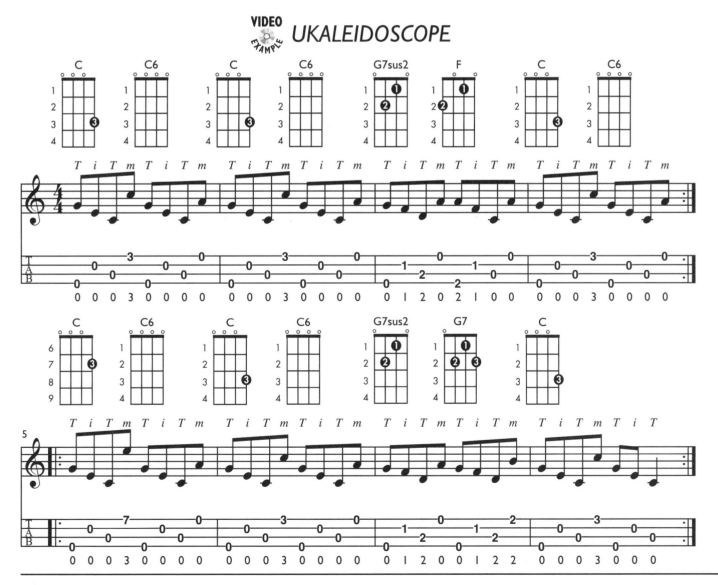

CHAPTER 11

Getting Ready for the Next Level

MUSICAL EXPRESSION

EXPRESSION

Music is not just about keeping time and playing the right notes or chords. In order for music to have an emotional effect, it needs a sense of *expression*. Two very important elements of musical expression are *phrasing* and *dynamics*.

PHRASING

Phrasing is the way that touch, volume, and tempo are used to imply a sense of direction, movement, and rest in a piece of music. If notes are like words, then phrasing is the way that the words are made to sound like sentences, or complete thoughts.

Phrase Markings

Written music uses a number of markings and terms to communicate phrasing and expression to the performer. Many of these terms are in Italian. A quick tour of a few commonly used terms should give you some ideas for your own music. First, the *phrase mark* is a curved line that loosely connects a passage of music. It can be confused with a slur or a tie, but the phrase mark is usually shown above the staff and may have slurs or ties beneath it.

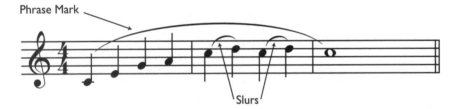

More About Phrases

- **Add your own phrase marks:** Phrase marks are sometimes shown in sheet music to give a detailed description of how the passage is to be expressed. You can also add your own phrase markings to help you break up a longer passage into smaller thoughts. This helps you learn it more quickly by working on smaller chunks of music at a time.

- **Common phrase lengths:** Musical phrases are very often two, four, or eight measures long. Four-bar phrases are probably the most common length, especially in vocal songs where four measures is the standard length for a line or two of lyrics.

- **Phrases don't always start on beat 1**: Sometimes phrases start on pickup notes before beat 1 (page 27). Often, if there are several phrases in a row, they may all have pickup notes.

- **Phrases create a sense of dialog:** Musical thoughts sometimes mirror the construction of speech. Two musical phrases might be paired together to form a musical "question and answer." Just as phrases are often two or four bars long, phrases themselves often appear in groups of two or four. Groups of phrases form larger sections of the form, like verses, choruses, and other types of sections.

OTHER PHRASING AND EXPRESSION TERMS

TERM	DEFINITION	MARKING
Legato	Notes are to be played in a smooth, connected fashion.	The word "Legato" marked above the music.
Staccato	Short, detached, unconnected notes.	The word "Staccato" marked above the music, or small dots above or below individual note heads.
Accent	A note played louder than the surrounding notes.	This sign > above or below the note head.

DYNAMICS

Dynamics define how loud or soft the notes or passages of music will sound. Dynamic expression and contrast are very important to imparting a sense of emotion in a piece of music.

LOUD			SOFT		
Mark	**Term**	**Definition**	**Mark**	**Term**	**Definition**
mf	Mezzo Forte	Medium Loud	*mp*	Mezzo Piano	Medium soft
f	Forte	Loud	*p*	Piano	Soft
ff	Fortissimo	Very Loud	*pp*	Pianissimo	Very soft
fff	Fortississimo	Very, very loud	*ppp*	Pianississimo	Very, very soft
<	Crescendo	Gradually becoming louder	>	Decrescendo	Gradually becoming softer

THE DYNAMIC SCALE

Arranged from softest to loudest, the dynamic markings look like this:

Softest   *Loudest*

ppp   *pp*   *p*   *mp*   *mf*   *ff*   *fff*

THE "ARCH"

Often, a phrase or an entire piece of music will lend itself to a dynamic "arch" that begins at a softer dynamic, climaxes at a louder dynamic, then returns to a softer level. This is especially true if the melody moves from low notes up to high notes, then back down. Look for opportunities to place this kind of expression in your music. Also, look for spots where a "reverse arch" (loud to soft to loud) might work.

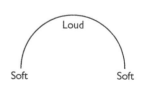

APPENDIX

LOW-G TUNING

The examples in this book have all utilized the reentrant tuning of G–C–E–A, where the 4th string, G, is tuned a whole step below the 1st string, A. This is also known as "high-G tuning." Another tuning is the "low-G" tuning, where the 4th string is tuned an octave lower than the standard tuning. This extends the range of the uke down a perfect 4th.

Low-G tuning can be used on any size ukulele. You will have to buy a special low-G set of strings, or a single low-G 4th string, as the string gauge of a high-G 4th string is too small to tune down a full octave without getting floppy. It's not very convenient to re-string the 4th string to switch back and forth. Many players keep a separate uke set up for low-G tuning all the time. Low-G tuning is popular for jazz improvisation and solo arrangements. A concert or tenor-size uke tuned to low-G will let you take advantage of the longer neck and greater fret access needed for more complex music.

HOW TO TUNE TO LOW-G TUNING
Below are the notes and matching frets (shown in parentheses) for both high-G tuning and low-G tuning, so you can see the difference.

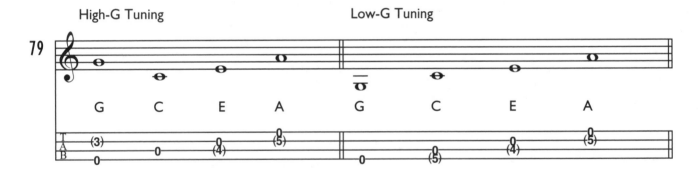

C MAJOR SCALE AND CHORDS
Following is a C Major scale in low-G tuning. In high-G tuning, the lowest note available is middle C. In low-G tuning, you get three extra scale steps below middle C. Not only does this improve the range of the C scale, but it makes it possible to play with greater range in all keys and positions. The C, F, and G chords are the I, IV, and V chords of the key of C. You can use the same fingerings you learned in standard tuning, but the notes produced are in a different voicing, giving more depth and range to each chord.

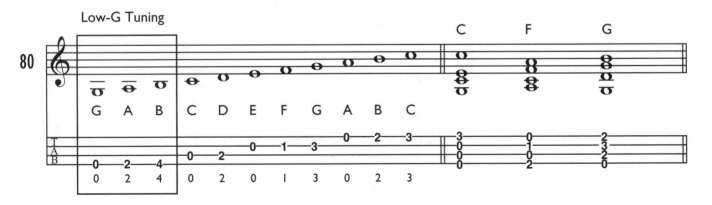

HOW TO PRACTICE

It is important from the beginning to play with the best, most relaxed technique you can. Though you will see and learn many variations of technique, this will become the "home base" to which your body will always return. Building these good habits requires two elements:

1. **Technique Exercises**
   These allow you to concentrate on technique without worrying about keeping your place in the music.

2. **Mental Focus**
   When you work on new songs or skills, be aware of your hand positions, body posture, rhythm, and touch.

WHEN TO PRACTICE

When you are first beginning, or when you are learning new skills, it is best to practice often. Five to ten minutes here and there on a new skill will work much better than an hour every three or four days. If you're lucky enough to be able to practice at the same time every day, you will see great improvement. You will also notice that you develop a better ability to focus on ukulele playing at that time. If it's not possible to practice at the same time every day, at least try to pick up the instrument for a few minutes every day, and then reinforce with longer sessions every couple of days.

WHAT TO PRACTICE

It is a great idea to have a small number of different "projects" going on in your practice sessions. This keeps you from feeling bored or bogged down and helps you improve several skills at once. Pick two or three things to work on every day for a week, then adjust your plan for the next week. Some of these projects might include reading music, learning to improvise, playing a new melody or learning a new chord progression. Be sure to spend time on each project every time you play.

ORGANIZING A PRACTICE SESSION

Here's a sample 30-minute practice session you may want to try for a few weeks. If you have more or less time, adjust the time on each item, while still visiting each item in every session.

1. **Technical Exercises** *5 minutes*
   These include finger exercises, counting and foot-tapping practice, warm-ups, and scales.

2. **Reading Music/Melody** *10 minutes*
   Try reading lots of new material in order to keep your reading skills in shape. If you are not working on reading music, work on melody playing and improvising.

3. **Playing Melodies/Chords** *10 minutes*
   Spend some time every day working on new songs you are learning to strum, pick, or play melodies to. Give extra attention to new chord forms and rhythms that may need several successive practice sessions to improve.

4. **Reviewing Old Material** *5 minutes*
   Always save a little time to go back and play songs you already play well. This keeps them "tuned up" and ready to go for times when you want to play for relaxation or with other people.

BUY A METRONOME

A *metronome* is an adjustable device that generates a beat pulse for you to play along with. Wind-up or battery-powered metronomes are available, as well as many downloadable apps. You can adjust the pulse from very slow to very fast. The speed is marked in beats-per-minute. A metronome speed of 60 is the same as one beat per second. The simplest metronomes make a ticking sound, while the more involved ones will make drum sounds and even mark measures for you.

When used regularly (and with a Zen-like patience), the metronome will help you learn to play with a steady rhythm. The only practice technique that is as valuable is to play with another person who has good rhythm—this can be difficult to do on a daily basis.

Don't let the metronome drive you crazy! At first, it may seem to be speeding up and slowing down while you play. Listen carefully—it's probably you. Pick a consistent, slow tempo to work with for the first few days and use the metronome while practicing one favorite song. See how many measures you can play before you and the metronome have a parting of the ways. Gradually increase your endurance before you increase the speed.

CONCLUSION AND RESOURCES FOR FURTHER STUDY

Thanks for choosing this book to get you started on the ukulele! You can have years of fun with what you've learned here, but there is also so much more. Check out *Intermediate Ukulele* and *Mastering Ukulele* for more chords, rhythms, scales, techniques, theory, and styles to take you on toward ukulele virtuosity. Remember to play every chance you get, and happy picking!

Books on Ukulele History
The 'Ukulele: a history by Jim Tranquada and John King, University of Hawai'i Press. ©2012
The Ukulele: A Visual History by Jim Beloff, Backstreet Books. Published by Mel Bay. ©1997–2003
              United Entertainment Media

Websites
The Internet is always changing, but there are all kinds of resources available if you search around a bit. The Ukulele Underground, a world-wide community forum of ukulele enthusiasts discussing a wide range of topics, is a great place to start (link current at time of writing):
            http://www.ukuleleunderground.com/forum/forum.php

In addition to other players mentioned in this book, here are just a few more players to check out. Look for their Websites and videos, buy their recordings, and keep an eye out for the next generation of influences!

Ukulele Giants of the Past
  Roy Smeck
  Tessie O'Shea
  Andy Cummings

Modern Players

Jason Arimoto	Brittni Paiva
Jim Beloff	Lyle Ritz
Benny Chong	Steven Sproat
Andy Eastwood	Brian Tolentino
Kimo Hussey	Byron Yasui
Eddie Kamae	The Sweet Hollywaiians
John King	The Ukulele Orchestra of Great Britain
Gordon Mark	The Wellington International Ukulele
Marcy Marxer	Orchestra